TEST BANK/ASSESSMENT PACKAGE

to accompany

McWhorter

College Reading and Study Skills
Ninth Edition

Kathleen T. McWhorter
Niagara County Community College

Jeanne M. Jones

PEARSON
Longman

NOTE REGARDING WEB SITES AND PASSWORDS:

If you need a password to access instructor supplements on a
Longman book-specific Web site, please use the following
information:

Username: awlbook
Password: adopt

Test Bank to accompany McWhorter, *College Reading and Study Skills, Ninth Edition*

Copyright ©2004 Pearson Education, Inc.

ISBN: 0-321-10453-6

1 2 3 4 5 6 7 8 9 10–DPC–06 05 04 03

TABLE OF CONTENTS

Introduction

Part One: Chapter Review Quizzes–Test Bank 1

Part Two: Chapter Review Quizzes–Test Bank 2

Part Three: Mastery Tests

Part Four: Additional Practice Exercises

INTRODUCTION

This assessment package contains two types of assessment for each chapter in *College Reading and Study Skills*, ninth edition: chapter review quizzes and mastery tests. These alternative measurements provide the instructor with a variety of opportunities to assess students' ability to learn and apply the techniques and strategies presented in the text. This package also includes additional practice exercises for vocabulary, using context and word parts, and comprehension, identifying main ideas and details.

CHAPTER REVIEW QUIZZES

The chapter review quizzes are primarily intended to provide an assessment of students' knowledge and comprehension of chapter content.

There are two sets of chapter review quizzes. Each set includes a ten-item, multiple-choice quiz for each chapter. Although the concepts tested in each set are similar, the test questions are different.

An answer key is provided for each multiple-choice test.

Coverage

It is the purpose of the chapter review quizzes to assess whether students have acquired a foundational knowledge of each chapter's content to enable them to apply the skill. Although the focus of each quiz is knowledge and comprehension of chapter content, quizzes do include application questions that provide hypothetical situations for evaluating students' ability to apply the skill.

Instructional Uses

Although the quizzes are intended as assessment tools, they can be used instructionally in several different ways:
1. Treat the quiz as an open-book exam, allowing students to locate the answers in the text. This activity will provide students with the opportunity to review chapter content and realize what skills are emphasized.
2. Ask students to predict or write questions they think will be on the quiz and then compare their predictions with the actual quiz. This activity will help students to determine what is important in each chapter, as well as to develop an important test-taking strategy.
3. Treat each quiz as a collaborative learning activity. Students can discuss each item and identify sections in the chapter that establish their choices as correct.
4. Use the quiz as a chapter preview. Allow students to skim or read the quiz questions before reading the chapter. The questions will establish an intent to remember chapter content.

MASTERY TESTS

The mastery tests are designed to measure students' ability to apply the skills learned in each chapter. These multiple-choice tests are intended to be practical, realistic simulations of reading and study situations that college students face. For the instructor's convenience, these tests were written to be self-scored, although instructors may elect to score these tests themselves. An answer key is provided for each test.

Coverage

Not all skills covered in a given chapter have been tested on the mastery test. Instead, the tests focus on the essential skills taught in each chapter. It was not possible to include skills that are too complex or time-consuming to measure within a testing situation.

Some mastery tests contain more than one part, each measuring a different skill. Each part could be administered separately, or given as a separate mastery test.

Instructional Uses

Although the mastery tests are intended as assessment tools, they can be used as instructional tools as well:

1. Use the mastery tests as collaborative learning activities in which students work together to complete the task(s) in each mastery test.
2. Use the mastery tests as additional practice exercises. Some students may require additional guided practice in learning and applying the particular skills taught. The tests are also appropriate for students who are not coregistered for other academic courses and, thus, are unable to complete the Academic Application exercises in the text.

ADDITIONAL PRACTICE EXERCISES

The additional practice exercises are designed to supplement the practice material included in *College Reading and Study Skills*. All exercises use a multiple-choice format for ease of scoring.

Coverage

Exercises are provided for vocabulary, using context and word parts, and for comprehension, identifying main ideas and details.

Instructional Uses

There are a variety of ways the exercises can be used to supplement exercises in the text:

1. Exercises may be assigned selectively to students who fail chapter quizzes or mastery tests on Chapters 6 or 12.
2. Exercises may be assigned as homework, after exercises in the text have been completed in class.

3. Exercises may be used as collaborative in-class or out-of-class activities.
4. Exercises may be assigned to students who are absent from class when a particular skill is taught or to those who request additional practice before taking the chapter quiz or mastery test.
5. The exercises may be used as student self-tests. Allow students to work through the practice exercises to determine if they are prepared to take the mastery tests on Chapters 6 or 12.

Although the exercises are primarily intended as additional practice, they may also be converted to a test format and used as additional quizzes, mastery tests, midterm exams, or final exams.

PART ONE

CHAPTER REVIEW QUIZZES—TEST BANK 1

CHAPTER 1
SETTING GOALS AND MANAGING YOUR TIME

Directions: *Write the letter of the choice that best completes each statement in the space provided.*

_____ 1. If Paula takes 15 hours of classes next semester, she should expect to study each week for about
   a. 7 ½ hours.
   b. 10 hours.
   c. 15 hours.
   d. 30 hours.

_____ 2. In defining your goals, you should do all of the following *except*
   a. be specific and detailed.
   b. set realistic, achievable goals.
   c. focus on what you want to avoid.
   d. establish a time frame.

_____ 3. A term plan lists all of your
   a. unchanging commitments.
   b. specific study times.
   c. homework assignments.
   d. leisure activities.

_____ 4. In managing your time effectively, the first step you should take is to
   a. set your priorities.
   b. analyze your time commitments.
   c. create a weekly schedule.
   d. sign up for extracurricular activities.

_____ 5. When you are constructing your weekly schedule, it is *least* effective to
   a. estimate the amount of time you will need for each course.
   b. plan to study your easiest subjects first.
   c. build short breaks into your schedule.
   d. schedule several short blocks of study time rather than one long block.

6. All of the following are effective time-saving techniques *except*
   a. using a word processor to write papers.
   b. combining daily activities with class assignments.
   c. using spare time as study time.
   d. making appointments in person rather than using the telephone.

7. One way to overcome a tendency to procrastinate is to
   a. list what needs to be done and in what order.
   b. spend some time away from your desk running errands.
   c. avoid projects or assignments that you are unsure of.
   d. leave the television on during your study time.

8. The best time to study for a physics class on Thursday morning is
   a. Tuesday morning.
   b. Wednesday evening.
   c. Friday evening.
   d. the weekend.

9. After studying one assignment for an hour, you should plan to
   a. keep going for at least another hour before taking a break.
   b. take a one-hour break.
   c. take a ten-minute break.
   d. put the assignment aside until the next day.

10. Of the following tasks associated with writing a term paper, the best one to work on when you are tired is
    a. researching the topic.
    b. writing the introduction.
    c. alphabetizing the bibliography.
    d. writing the conclusion.

CHAPTER 2
LEARNING STYLE AND LEARNING STRATEGIES

Directions: *Write the letter of the choice that best completes each statement in the space provided.*

_____ 1. The most important reason to identify your learning style is that it can help you
   a. accept your style as fixed and unchanging.
   b. understand how to study more effectively.
   c. improve your scores on other, more formal tests of learning style.
   d. decide what time of day is best for studying.

_____ 2. The learning strategy that would be most appropriate for both visual and spatial learners would be
   a. drawing diagrams and charts.
   b. tape-recording lectures.
   c. writing summaries.
   d. talking aloud when studying.

_____ 3. After taking the Learning Style Questionnaire, Sarah wanted to find out if she learns better by listening or by seeing. She should look at her score on the
   a. auditory/visual section.
   b. applied/conceptual section.
   c. social/independent section.
   d. creative/pragmatic section.

_____ 4. The spatial/verbal section of the Learning Style Questionnaire reveals
   a. your ability to visualize how things work or how they are positioned in space.
   b. whether practical applications are necessary for your understanding of ideas.
   c. your preferred level of interaction with other people in the learning process.
   d. whether you prefer to learn by taking risks or following rules.

_____ 5. One way that learning in college differs from high school is that, in college,
   a. weekly class time is much longer.
   b. instructors spend more time providing reviews of course content.
   c. learning is limited to memorizing a collection of facts.
   d. students are expected to evaluate new ideas before accepting or rejecting them.

6. An active approach to learning would involve
    a. memorizing lecture notes.
    b. rereading textbook assignments.
    c. considering the purpose behind assignments.
    d. doing only what is expected to get a good grade.

7. According to the progression of thinking skills developed by Benjamin Bloom, the highest level of thinking is
    a. knowledge.
    b. comprehension.
    c. analysis.
    d. evaluation.

8. If an English instructor wanted to give an assignment at the application level of thinking, she might ask students to
    a. compare two poems by the same author.
    b. edit a poorly punctuated paragraph.
    c. evaluate the effectiveness of an essay about writing.
    d. define a list of grammatical terms.

9. Synthesis is defined as the level of thinking in which a person
    a. puts ideas and information together to create something new.
    b. applies knowledge to a new situation.
    c. assesses the value or worth of information.
    d. repeats information with no changes.

10. Of the following questions, the one that requires you to think at the knowledge level of thinking is
    a. What information do I need to learn?
    b. How can I use this information?
    c. How are the ideas in this material related?
    d. Is this information accurate, reliable, and valuable?

CHAPTER 3
UNDERSTANDING HOW LEARNING AND MEMORY WORK

Directions: *Write the letter of the choice that best completes each statement in the space provided.*

_____ 1. Daniel spent his afternoon break reading a chapter in his business law textbook. According to the retention curve, after about an hour Daniel will be able to recall
  a. almost everything he read.
  b. about half of what he read.
  c. only dates and numbers.
  d. hardly any of what he read.

_____ 2. The process through which information enters the brain is known as
  a. encoding.
  b. sensory storage.
  c. retrieval.
  d. information transfer.

_____ 3. Information is retained in your short-term memory for
  a. less than a minute.
  b. about an hour.
  c. 8-10 hours.
  d. 24 hours.

_____ 4. When your brain automatically sorts out important information from trivial signals, it is engaging in
  a. the Number Seven Theory.
  b. rote learning.
  c. schema development.
  d. selective attention.

_____ 5. The function of sensory storage is to
  a. retain information until it is sent to short-term memory or discarded.
  b. rearrange information into groups or sets.
  c. allow you to practice information to learn it.
  d. store information indefinitely.

_____ 6. Of the following activities, the one that best illustrates the use of recoding is
  a. memorizing the exact definition of a word.
  b. taking notes in a lecture.
  c. highlighting information in a textbook.
  d. solving a math problem.

5

_____ 7. Elaborative rehearsal primarily involves
    a. thinking about and reacting to information.
    b. repeating information to learn it in a fixed order.
    c. monitoring the capacity of short-term memory.
    d. rearranging information through different sensory channels.

_____ 8. For an anatomy test, Rosa made up a rhyme to remember the parts of the brain. In this situation, Rosa was using a strategy called
    a. periodic review.
    b. elaboration.
    c. mnemonics.
    d. association.

_____ 9. Megan has been working on an economics chapter for several hours. When she finishes, the most effective way for her to store that information is to
    a. move on immediately to another subject.
    b. start at the beginning and reread the entire chapter.
    c. reread each chapter heading and the summary.
    d. review her lecture notes from her economics class.

_____ 10. Developing retrieval clues involves
    a. creating a detailed mental image of information you want to learn.
    b. selecting a word or phrase that summarizes several pieces of information.
    c. connecting new information with personal experience.
    d. simulating test conditions.

CHAPTER 4
TAKING NOTES IN CLASS

Directions: *Write the letter of the choice that best completes each statement in the space provided.*

_____ 1. In each waking hour, the average adult is likely to spend the most time
   a. listening.
   b. writing.
   c. reading.
   d. speaking.

_____ 2. One difference between listening and hearing is that hearing
   a. is an intellectual activity.
   b. involves the processing and interpretation of incoming information.
   c. is a passive, biological process.
   d. is intentional and deliberate.

_____ 3. All of the following suggestions can help you improve your listening skills *except*
   a. focusing on content, not delivery.
   b. concentrating on remembering separate, unconnected facts.
   c. being alert for transitions.
   d. trying to understand the lecturer's purpose.

_____ 4. As compared to the average rate of speech, the rate of thinking is about
   a. the same.
   b. half as fast.
   c. twice as fast.
   d. four times as fast.

_____ 5. An effective set of lecture notes should do all of the following *except*
   a. serve as a record of the lecture's main points.
   b. include enough examples so that the information can be recalled later.
   c. show the organization of the lecture.
   d. include everything the lecturer said.

6. Kendra is listening to her biology instructor give a lecture. During the lecture, Kendra probably will be able to pick out important ideas by all of the following signals from her instructor *except*
   a. nonverbal clues.
   b. an increase in the instructor's rate of speech.
   c. repeated mention of specific topics.
   d. audiovisual aids.

7. If you are using indentation to show a lecture's organization, the item that should be indented the *most* is
   a. a major topic.
   b. a main idea.
   c. a detail.
   d. an example.

8. The most effective way to review your notes after a lecture is to
   a. edit your notes as soon as possible.
   b. wait a few days and then reread your notes aloud.
   c. recopy your notes to make them more legible.
   d. transcribe your notes from a tape recording.

9. Julie is trying a new system to improve the way she reviews and studies her lecture notes. After she has edited her notes, she fills in the left margin with words and phrases that summarize her notes and help trigger her memory. This information indicates that Julie is using
   a. enumeration.
   b. pragmatic editing.
   c. mnemonic devices.
   d. the recall clue system.

10. Lee arrived for a lecture class and talked with friends until the lecture began. A more effective use of his time would have been to
    a. review the homework assignment due that day.
    b. begin reading the next textbook chapter.
    c. review his notes from the previous lecture.
    d. discuss the instructor's lecturing style with a classmate.

CHAPTER 5
ACTIVE READING STRATEGIES

Directions: *Write the letter of the choice that best completes each statement in the space provided.*

_____   1.   The primary purpose of prereading is to
   a.   discover how you feel about the material.
   b.   memorize important facts and details.
   c.   identify the most important ideas in the material.
   d.   evaluate the author's qualifications.

_____   2.   During prereading, it is most important to
   a.   record your impression of the material.
   b.   create a detailed outline of the material.
   c.   skip over graphical aids.
   d.   read each major heading.

_____   3.   The first sentence under each heading in a chapter typically provides the
   a.   central thought.
   b.   author's biographical information.
   c.   author's opinion.
   d.   summary.

_____   4.   Prereading is most useful when reading
   a.   novels.
   b.   poems.
   c.   short stories.
   d.   textbooks.

_____   5.   In general, predictions made before reading should be
   a.   based only on the chapter preview.
   b.   based only on the chapter summary.
   c.   revised, confirmed, or rejected while reading.
   d.   concerned only with the chapter's content, not its organization.

6. Ellis wants to find out what he already knows about monopolies before he reads the chapter in his marketing textbook. He decides to free-associate, which means that he plans to
   a. ask himself questions about monopolies and then try to answer them.
   b. write down everything he can think of about monopolies.
   c. look in other sources for information about monopolies.
   d. interview other people for information about monopolies.

7. For an art history textbook chapter titled "The End of the Renaissance," the most effective guide question would be
   a. When did the Renaissance take place?
   b. Who were the major artists of the Renaissance?
   c. Where did the Renaissance take place?
   d. What were the contributing factors that led to the end of the Renaissance?

8. One way you can assess your comprehension of material is to look for a positive signal, such as
   a. everything in the material seems important.
   b. you often slow down or reread.
   c. you can paraphrase the author's ideas.
   d. the vocabulary seems unfamiliar.

9. The primary purpose of checkpoints is to
   a. provide a preview of the text.
   b. generate guide questions.
   c. allow you to evaluate your learning.
   d. create a mental outline of the text.

10. All of the following techniques can help you improve your comprehension *except*
    a. reading aloud difficult sentences.
    b. increasing your reading rate.
    c. rereading complicated sections.
    d. writing notes in the margins.

CHAPTER 6
UNDERSTANDING PARAGRAPHS

Directions: *Write the letter of the choice that best completes each statement in the space provided.*

_____ 1. In a paragraph, all details are
    a. related to the paragraph's main idea.
    b. essential to the author's argument.
    c. intended to repeat or restate the main idea.
    d. meant to provide primary supporting evidence.

_____ 2. The topic of a paragraph can be defined as the
    a. author's point of view.
    b. first sentence of the paragraph.
    c. subject of the whole paragraph.
    d. paragraph's supporting details.

_____ 3. One clue to the topic of a paragraph is the
    a. repeated use of a word throughout the paragraph.
    b. types of details in the paragraph.
    c. frequency of examples in the paragraph.
    d. way the paragraph is organized.

_____ 4. An author who uses a deductive thought pattern in a paragraph typically
    a. states the main idea at the beginning of the paragraph.
    b. builds up to the main idea and states it in the middle of the paragraph.
    c. builds up to the main idea and states it at the end of the paragraph.
    d. does not directly state the main idea in any one sentence.

_____ 5. The type of transition that indicates a connection between two or more things is known as
    a. time-sequence.
    b. cause-effect.
    c. continuation.
    d. summation.

_____ 6. The phrase "on the other hand" is an example of the type of transition known as
    a. example.
    b. cause-effect.
    c. contrast.
    d. summation.

_____ 7. Enumeration is a type of transition in which the author
  a. indicates that an example will follow.
  b. arranges ideas in the order in which they happened.
  c. marks or identifies each major point to suggest order of importance.
  d. shows how the previous idea is similar to what follows.

_____ 8. The three essential elements of a paragraph are its topic, its main idea, and its
  a. topic sentence.
  b. supporting details.
  c. transitions.
  d. structure.

_____ 9. If the main idea of a paragraph is not stated in a topic sentence, the reader should
  a. move on to the next paragraph.
  b. view the paragraph as transitional only.
  c. try to identify the topic and then reason out the paragraph's main idea.
  d. determine whether the paragraph is the author's opinion only.

_____ 10. Of the following sentences, the one most likely to be a topic sentence and not a detail is
  a. Bone is one of the hardest materials in the body.
  b. First, consider the effects of calcium on the diet.
  c. For example, older women often experience osteoporosis.
  d. In contrast, cartilage is a type of connective tissue.

CHAPTER 7
FOLLOWING THOUGHT PATTERNS

Directions: *Write the letter of the choice that best completes each statement in the space provided.*

_____ 1. In contrast to the main idea of a paragraph, the controlling idea in a textbook section typically
a. is more specific.
b. is less comprehensive.
c. relies on fewer supporting details.
d. takes many paragraphs to explain.

_____ 2. In most textbooks, the progression of ideas typically goes from
a. general to particular.
b. small to large.
c. opinion to fact.
d. inductive to deductive.

_____ 3. The body of an essay usually presents the essay's
a. thesis statement.
b. controlling idea.
c. supporting ideas and information.
d. summary.

_____ 4. The primary purpose of an example is to
a. show how a concept can be applied in a real situation.
b. give reasons to support the writer's opinion.
c. compare and contrast two different ideas.
d. persuade the reader to accept an idea.

_____ 5. Words that indicate a pattern of thought are called
a. maps.
b. schemata.
c. directional words.
d. definitions.

_____ 6. Jacob is writing a term paper for his botany class in which he defines the word "monocot." According to the standard pattern, the first part of his definition should
   a. explain that monocots belong to the general class of "plants."
   b. describe characteristics of monocots.
   c. give examples of various types of monocots.
   d. explain how monocots differ from other plants, such as dicots.

_____ 7. Directional words such as "first" and "finally" typically indicate the organizational pattern called
   a. definition.
   b. time sequence.
   c. cause-effect.
   d. problem-solution.

_____ 8. Of the following topics, the one most likely to be developed using the comparison-contrast pattern is the
   a. two types of leaders found in organizations.
   b. parts and functions of the human ear.
   c. steps to follow in grasping a novel's theme.
   d. purpose and content of a resume.

_____ 9. Of the following topics, the one that would most likely be developed using the problem-solution pattern is
   a. extrasensory perception (ESP).
   b. the discovery of America.
   c. overcrowding of classrooms.
   d. the life cycle of a butterfly.

_____ 10. Of the following directional phrases, the one most likely to indicate a problem-solution pattern is
   a. if . . . then.
   b. as well as.
   c. by contrast.
   d. for example.

CHAPTER 8
READING GRAPHICS AND TECHNICAL WRITING

Directions: *Write the letter of the choice that best completes each statement in the space provided.*

_____ 1. When you are reading pages with graphics, you should remember that
   a. graphics are unimportant if they are accompanied by text.
   b. captions and titles should be ignored.
   c. graphics are often more important than the paragraphs that surround them.
   d. stopping to read the graphics will interrupt the flow of reading and slow you down.

_____ 2. When you study a table, you should do all of the following *except*
   a. draw conclusions.
   b. make comparisons.
   c. ignore unusual increases or decreases.
   d. look for trends.

_____ 3. The type of graph that would be most appropriate for showing the percentage of women who work outside the home is a
   a. stacked bar graph.
   b. multiple bar graph.
   c. linear graph.
   d. continuous data graph.

_____ 4. Milo has created a linear graph showing the relationship between years of education and frequency of traffic citations. His graph shows a negative relationship between the two variables, meaning that as years of education increase, the frequency of traffic citations
   a. also increases.
   b. decreases.
   c. remains the same.
   d. is unaffected.

_____ 5. For a political science project, Gerard wants to create a chart showing the process by which an immigrant becomes a U.S. citizen. The best way for Gerard to show this information would be in
   a. a flowchart.
   b. an organizational chart.
   c. a pictogram.
   d. a pie chart.

6. Reading diagrams differs from reading other types of graphics in that diagrams
   a. often correspond to fairly large segments of text.
   b. are seldom used in technical or scientific texts.
   c. use symbols or drawings to make statistics seem realistic.
   d. are intended primarily to elicit an emotional response.

7. One feature on a map that typically does not appear in other graphics is
   a. a caption.
   b. distance scales.
   c. trends.
   d. units of measurements.

8. Photographs are often included in a text to
   a. reveal trends.
   b. organize information.
   c. explain processes.
   d. elicit an emotional response.

9. When you are reading technical writing, you should do all of the following *except*
   a. read at about twice the speed you use with nontechnical writing.
   b. preread carefully.
   c. read the material at least twice.
   d. visualize what is being described.

10. One characteristic of technical writing is that it typically
    a. contains very few graphics.
    b. does not use examples or sample problems.
    c. presents a great many facts as compactly as possible.
    d. avoids introducing specialized vocabulary.

CHAPTER 9
READING AND EVALUATING ELECTRONIC SOURCES

Directions: *Write the letter of the choice that best completes each statement in the space provided.*

_____ 1. All of the following statements about electronic sources are true *except*
   a. electronic sources must be read differently than print sources.
   b. college instructors often expect their students to use electronic sources.
   c. computers are an important means of communication in the workplace.
   d. the Internet is always the most reliable source of information.

_____ 2. The primary purpose of an Internet service provider (ISP) is to
   a. provide technical support for your computer software.
   b. connect your computer to the Internet.
   c. help you locate information about a specific topic.
   d. offer reviews or evaluations of different Web sites.

_____ 3. When you want to browse the Web using general topics, the most appropriate search tool is a
   a. subject directory.
   b. search engine.
   c. meta-search engine.
   d. site map.

_____ 4. The sponsor of a Web site is the person or organization who
   a. designed the site.
   b. provided the links to related sites.
   c. wrote the material included on the site.
   d. paid for the site to be created and placed on the Web.

_____ 5. The address of a Web site that is sponsored by a nonprofit organization typically ends with the abbreviation
   a. biz.
   b. edu.
   c. org.
   d. info.

_____ 6. One indication that an Internet source contains accurate information is that the
   a. author's professional credentials are not part of the site.
   b. information on the site is comparable to print sources on the same topic.
   c. site is sponsored by an educational or nonprofit organization.
   d. site does not provide links to other Web sites.

_____ 7. One way that hypertext differs from traditional print text is that hypertext typically
   a. depends on other pages for meaning.
   b. progresses in a single direction only.
   c. allows readers to acquire information in different sequences.
   d. provides more initial feedback about what the page contains.

_____ 8. When you are visiting a Web site, it is most important to
   a. concentrate on the words and ignore the graphics.
   b. scroll down to see the next page.
   c. follow as many links as possible.
   d. focus on your purpose for visiting the site.

_____ 9. Compared to traditional sources, online communication tends to be
   a. more detailed.
   b. more concise.
   c. less visual.
   d. less flexible.

_____ 10. All of the following are examples of plagiarism _except_
   a. using information from the Internet without listing the source.
   b. paraphrasing an author's words without giving the author credit.
   c. using commonly known facts without documentation.
   d. accidentally omitting quotation marks when quoting an author.

CHAPTER 10
CRITICAL THINKING AND READING

Directions: *Write the letter of the choice that best completes each statement in the space provided.*

_____ 1. An inference can be described best as a
   a. fact.
   b. generalization.
   c. negative opinion.
   d. reasoned guess.

_____ 2. All of the following questions indicate a higher level of thinking *except*
   a. What are the author's qualifications?
   b. Is the material fact or opinion?
   c. What is the literal meaning of the material?
   d. What is the author's purpose?

_____ 3. Julian plans to write a term paper about the long-term effects of rapid weight loss in young adults. Of the following sources, the most reliable one would be
   a. a brochure from a weight loss clinic.
   b. an article in a teen entertainment magazine.
   c. an Internet chat room discussion of anorexia.
   d. an article in a medical journal.

_____ 4. In textbooks, the author's qualifications typically appear
   a. on the title page or in the preface.
   b. on the book jacket.
   c. in the index.
   d. in the table of contents.

_____ 5. The primary difference between a fact and an opinion is that a fact
   a. is always true.
   b. expresses a feeling or belief.
   c. is not a reliable source of information.
   d. can be verified.

6. Of the following statements, the best example of an informed opinion is
   a. Traffic wouldn't be so bad if more people carpooled.
   b. According to a 1999 Department of Transportation report, more than 50,000 cars and trucks travel on Highway 5 each year.
   c. People who live within a mile of their jobs should walk or ride bicycles to work.
   d. The Environmental Protection Agency stated that air pollution could be significantly reduced if every commuter used mass transit once a week.

7. Recognizing an author's tone is most important because it
   a. reveals the author's attitude toward the subject.
   b. directly identifies the author's intended audience.
   c. provides the reader with objective information about the subject.
   d. establishes the author's credentials.

8. An article about professional sports included this statement: "With salaries already in the millions, professional athletes and their agents are doing their best to destroy the average fan's enjoyment of the game." In this example, the author's bias is evident through the use of the word
   a. millions.
   b. professional.
   c. destroy.
   d. average.

9. A successful argument is one that makes a claim about an issue and then
   a. explores each of the opposing viewpoints objectively.
   b. supports the claim with evidence.
   c. presents ideas in an emotional rather than logical manner.
   d. calls the audience to action.

10. The first step you should take when reading an argument is to
    a. identify the issue.
    b. highlight key evidence that supports the author's claim.
    c. evaluate the types of evidence the author provides.
    d. write a brief outline of the argument.

CHAPTER 11
EXPANDING YOUR VOCABULARY

Directions: *Write the letter of the choice that best completes each statement in the space provided.*

_____ 1. One of the best ways to improve your vocabulary is to
   a. read widely and diversely.
   b. focus your reading on technical subjects only.
   c. spend several hours each day memorizing the dictionary.
   d. start using words you cannot fully define.

_____ 2. William wants to find out more about the meaning of the word "intaglio" and how it is used in the field of art. The best place for him to look would be
   a. a pocket dictionary.
   b. a desk dictionary.
   c. a subject area dictionary.
   d. an unabridged dictionary.

_____ 3. With respect to vocabulary, most people have
   a. only one level, consisting of words they use in everyday speech or writing.
   b. two levels, including words they use and words they know but do not use.
   c. two levels, including words they use in speech and words they use in writing.
   d. at least four levels, varying in strength.

_____ 4. Maria is writing a speech in which she uses the word "artificial" several times. She would look up "artificial" in a thesaurus if she wanted to find out
   a. how to pronounce it properly.
   b. where it originated.
   c. how to say it in another language.
   d. what other words she could use to mean the same thing.

_____ 5. Specialized vocabulary includes words and phrases that
   a. have a different meaning in another language.
   b. are used in a particular subject area.
   c. must be defined each time they are used.
   d. are used casually in speech.

_____ 6. As compared to pocket dictionaries, desk dictionaries are typically
   a. less expensive.
   b. more inclusive.
   c. less detailed.
   d. more convenient.

_____ 7. In a textbook, the glossary is a
   a. vocabulary list at the beginning of each chapter.
   b. list of references at the end of the book.
   c. set of review questions at the end of each chapter.
   d. comprehensive list of terms at the end of the book.

_____ 8. Your last step in handling new terminology presented in a class lecture should be to
   a. organize the terms into an efficient system for learning them.
   b. edit your notes after the lecture.
   c. check each definition to be sure it is complete.
   d. add explanations and examples to your notes.

_____ 9. When you use the vocabulary card system, you should remember to
   a. always keep the cards in alphabetical order.
   b. review the entire pack of cards every time.
   c. put as many new terms on each card as possible.
   d. study the cards by trying to recall both meanings and terms.

_____ 10. A strong vocabulary is characterized by all of the following *except*
   a. using precise, descriptive language.
   b. applying technical terms in specific disciplines.
   c. using unusual meanings for common words.
   d. substituting long words for short words.

CHAPTER 12
USING CONTEXT AND WORD PARTS

Directions: *Write the letter of the choice that best completes each statement in the space provided.*

_____ 1. Isaac was reading his history textbook when he came to the word "proletariat." The first thing he should do to figure out the word's meaning is to
   a. look it up in the dictionary.
   b. break it up into parts.
   c. try to pronounce it out loud.
   d. look for context clues in the sentence.

_____ 2. Of the following words and phrases, the only one that does *not* indicate the use of a contrast context clue is
   a. on the other hand.
   b. for instance.
   c. however.
   d. whereas.

_____ 3. Using context clues in the logic of a passage involves figuring out the meaning of a word through
   a. general reasoning about the content of the sentence.
   b. a phrase in the sentence that has the opposite meaning.
   c. specific, concrete examples provided by the author.
   d. the author's direct statement of the word's meaning.

_____ 4. When you are learning word parts, you should remember that words
   a. are usually built on at least one root.
   b. can only have one prefix at a time.
   c. always have both a prefix and a suffix.
   d. always change in spelling when they are combined with suffixes.

Directions: *Each of the following sentences contains a word whose meaning can be determined from the context. Select the choice that most clearly states the meaning of the underlined word as it is used in the sentence.*

_____ 5. There was so much <u>detritus</u> from the hurricane that it was difficult to walk down the beach.
   a. rainfall
   b. trash and debris
   c. traffic
   d. holes

_____ 6. The soccer players appeared <u>crestfallen</u> as their star player limped off the field.
   a. hopeful
   b. excited
   c. dejected
   d. ashamed

_____ 7. The children looked angelic, but after their parents left they became more and more <u>obstreperous.</u>
   a. agreeable
   b. unruly or rowdy
   c. sad
   d. intellectual

Directions: *Each of the following underlined words contains a root and a prefix and/or suffix. Using your knowledge of roots, prefixes, and suffixes, choose the best definition for each word.*

_____ 8. Most of the defendant's responses were <u>monosyllabic.</u>
   a. insulting
   b. difficult to hear
   c. loud
   d. one syllable

_____ 9. Although the band's name was Harmony, it was a <u>misnomer.</u>
   a. problem
   b. wrong name
   c. nickname
   d. misprint

_____ 10. The students reacted to the assignment with <u>incredulity.</u>
   a. disbelief
   b. relief
   c. indifference
   d. excitement

CHAPTER 13
TEXTBOOK HIGHLIGHTING AND MARKING

Directions: *Write the letter of the choice that best completes each statement in the space provided.*

_____ 1. Highlighting is important for all of the following reasons *except*
a. it keeps you physically active while you read.
b. it forces you to evaluate what you read.
c. it eliminates your need to review the material.
d. it helps you see how the material is organized.

_____ 2. When you are highlighting a textbook, you should remember to
a. highlight supporting facts as well as main ideas.
b. skip over boldface headings.
c. highlight complete sentences.
d. highlight as quickly as you can.

_____ 3. In general, you should try to highlight no more than
a. one-tenth of each page.
b. one-third of each page.
c. one-half of each page.
d. two-thirds of each page.

_____ 4. Annie has finished highlighting the first chapter in her business management class. All of the following signs indicate that she has highlighted effectively *except* that
a. she has highlighted the right amount of information.
b. her highlighted passages read smoothly.
c. her highlighting accurately reflects the meaning of the passage.
d. she has varied her system of highlighting to keep it interesting.

_____ 5. As you read, the most effective way to show the relative importance of ideas and the relationships between ideas is through
a. highlighting only.
b. marking only.
c. a combination of highlighting and marking.
d. a combination of highlighting and rereading.

_____ 6. When you are marking information in a textbook, it is most important to
a. include comments on the author's style.
b. mark only the information that has not been highlighted.
c. make sure someone else can understand your notes.
d. think about the information and evaluate it as you read.

_____ 7. Summary notes are most effectively used in passages that contain
    a. simple concepts.
    b. brief examples.
    c. long and complicated ideas.
    d. graphics.

_____ 8. When you use summary notes, you should always
    a. refer to the chapter summary first.
    b. limit your notes to one or two words.
    c. highlight the section before you summarize it.
    d. use words that will trigger your memory.

_____ 9. Teresa is about to begin reading her new history textbook. The *least* effective use of Teresa's time would be for her to
    a. highlight important passages as she reads.
    b. make summary notes in the margins.
    c. mark possible test questions when she notices them.
    d. plan to reread the entire text when she has finished reading it once.

_____ 10. When you are reading a textbook passage, you would most likely mark or highlight all of the following *except*
    a. illustration credits.
    b. lists of ideas.
    c. definitions.
    d. unfamiliar words.

CHAPTER 14
METHODS OF ORGANIZING INFORMATION

Directions: *Write the letter of the choice that best completes each statement in the space provided.*

_____ 1. Methods of consolidating information include all of the following *except*
   a. outlining.
   b. summarizing.
   c. recopying ideas.
   d. mapping.

_____ 2. One characteristic of an effective outline is that
   a. it always uses complete sentences.
   b. it shows the relative importance of ideas.
   c. all the items fit into the outline format.
   d. information is copied directly from the text.

_____ 3. Outlining requires you to do all of the following *except*
   a. think about the material as you are outlining.
   b. sort out important ideas from those that are less important.
   c. express ideas in your own words.
   d. create examples to support the material.

_____ 4. Using standard outline format, the first entry indented under the heading "I. Major topic" should be
   a. "A. First major idea."
   b. "1. First important detail."
   c. "a. Example."
   d. "II. Second major idea."

_____ 5. Outlining would be appropriate for all of the following situations *except* for
   a. recording and sorting information about types of plants in a biology chapter.
   b. writing a critical interpretation of an essay on gun control.
   c. rereading basic definitions on a vocabulary list.
   d. organizing information about the sequence of commands in a data processing program.

_____ 6. As compared to an outline, a summary is typically
   a. more opinionated.
   b. less detailed.
   c. longer.
   d. less objective.

_____ 7. Your first step in writing a summary should be
   a. determining the author's attitude and approach toward the subject.
   b. locating and evaluating key supporting details.
   c. underlining or highlighting key terms and definitions.
   d. identifying the author's main idea and writing a statement that expresses it.

_____ 8. Of the following situations, writing a summary would be _least_ effective for
   a. preparing for an essay exam in history.
   b. recording the results of a chemistry experiment.
   c. learning the bones of the hand for an anatomy quiz.
   d. understanding the plot of a novel assigned in English class.

_____ 9. In Jim's psychology course, he is studying three substances used for mind alteration: stimulants, sedatives, and tranquilizers. For the next exam, he will be expected to know how these substances differ in dosage, physical effects, psychological dependence, and so on. The most effective way for Jim to study this information would be to
   a. prepare an outline for each substance.
   b. draw a process diagram.
   c. make a comparison-contrast chart.
   d. write a summary.

_____ 10. Of the following projects in a political science course, a time line would be most appropriate for showing the
   a. process by which a bill becomes a law.
   b. sequence of events leading up to the impeachment of President Clinton.
   c. chain of command in government, from the president on down.
   d. differences between the Democratic and Republican parties.

CHAPTER 15
STUDY AND REVIEW STRATEGIES

Directions: *Write the letter of the choice that best completes each statement in the space provided.*

_____ 1. The primary purpose of paraphrasing is to
   a. restate the author's meaning in your own words.
   b. express your opinion of the author's ideas.
   c. choose one or two of the author's statements as summaries.
   d. quote the author's main points.

_____ 2. Paraphrasing is useful in all of the following situations *except* when
   a. you want to be sure you understand difficult or complicated material.
   b. the text requires exact, detailed comprehension.
   c. you want to recall the author's exact words.
   d. the material is complex, poorly written, or overly formal.

_____ 3. In order to paraphrase effectively, it is most important for you to
   a. read quickly.
   b. paraphrase word by word.
   c. paraphrase as you read the material the first time.
   d. pay attention to relationships among ideas as you read.

_____ 4. The best types of questions to write for self-testing purposes are
   a. multiple-choice.
   b. matching.
   c. true/false.
   d. open-ended.

_____ 5. When you are self-testing in preparation for an exam, it is important to
   a. focus on writing questions that require factual recall only.
   b. always answer the questions the same day you write them.
   c. respond to the questions with short answers only.
   d. take time to review and critique your answers.

_____ 6. A learning journal is a written record of
   a. homework assignments.
   b. notes from lectures.
   c. study and review techniques.
   d. possible exam questions.

_____ 7. In the SQ3R system, the "S" step stands for
a. summarize.
b. survey.
c. study.
d. self-test.

_____ 8. During the recite step of SQ3R, you should be
a. rereading the assignment.
b. forming questions about each section.
c. checking your recall for each section.
d. answering the end-of-chapter questions.

_____ 9. One popular modification of the SQ3R system is the addition of a fourth "R," which recognizes the importance of
a. reacting.
b. tape recording.
c. writing and summarizing.
d. rereading and reviewing.

_____ 10. Darien wants to develop a specialized study-reading approach for each of his subjects. Of the following courses, he would be most likely to add Interpret and React steps to
a. business math.
b. contemporary fiction.
c. introduction to physics.
d. abnormal psychology.

CHAPTER 16
PREPARING FOR EXAMS

Directions: *Write the letter of the choice that best completes each statement in the space provided.*

_____ 1. The best way to prepare for an exam is to
   a. study new material the night before the exam so it's fresh in your mind.
   b. skip the class prior to the exam and spend the time studying instead.
   c. focus on reviewing basic facts and definitions that you already know.
   d. spend time organizing the material to be reviewed.

_____ 2. The *least* effective way to identify what to study for an exam is to
   a. review textbook chapters.
   b. memorize every item on old exams and quizzes.
   c. talk with classmates about the material.
   d. go over lecture notes.

_____ 3. If you discover that an instructor emphasizes application questions on exams, you should adjust your study methods to focus on
   a. factual review.
   b. out-of-class assignments.
   c. practical situations and uses.
   d. relationships between topics.

_____ 4. Synthesis is an important critical-thinking skill because it forces you to focus on
   a. facts.
   b. definitions.
   c. dates.
   d. relationships.

_____ 5. If you wanted to determine the progression of ideas in a course, you would probably look at all of the following *except* the
   a. course outline.
   b. syllabus.
   c. textbook's table of contents.
   d. vocabulary list.

_____ 6. Of the following types of information, a study sheet would be *least* useful for reviewing
   a. trends in ideas.
   b. theories and principles.
   c. groups of unrelated facts.
   d. the pros and cons of controversial issues.

_____ 7. The index card system is effective for all of the following reasons *except*
   a. it allows you to study in your spare time.
   b. it forces you to learn information in a certain order.
   c. you can separate the items you already know from the ones you have not yet learned.
   d. you can review your cards regularly until you have learned all the items.

_____ 8. The index card system is most appropriately used for
   a. understanding theories.
   b. learning brief facts.
   c. reviewing concepts and principles.
   d. studying cause-effect relationships.

_____ 9. Marta is preparing for an essay exam. The first thing she should do to prepare is
   a. select probable topics.
   b. create a key-word outline.
   c. write possible questions.
   d. recopy her lecture notes.

_____ 10. When you are predicting essay questions at the analysis level of thinking, you should ask questions that
   a. test your ability to take ideas apart.
   b. force you to look at similarities and differences.
   c. involve making judgments and assessing value.
   d. require you to recall facts.

CHAPTER 17
TAKING EXAMS

Directions: *Write the letter of the choice that best completes each statement in the space provided.*

_____ 1. One effective way to approach an exam is to
   a. arrive at least a half hour before the exam begins.
   b. sit in the back of the class.
   c. try to anticipate trick questions.
   d. get an overview of the exam before you answer any questions.

_____ 2. Gwen is taking an exam with a section of true/false questions worth 25 points, a section of multiple-choice questions worth 25 points, and two essay questions worth 50 points. She should plan to spend most of her time
   a. prereading and reviewing all the questions.
   b. answering the true/false questions.
   c. answering the multiple-choice questions.
   d. answering the essay questions.

_____ 3. If you encounter a difficult question on an objective exam, your best strategy is to
   a. leave it blank.
   b. leave it blank but mark the question so you can answer it later if you have time.
   c. enter your best guess and mark the question so you can return to it later.
   d. enter your top two guesses and mark the question so you can return to it later.

_____ 4. If you are unable to figure out the answer to a true/false item on an exam, you should probably mark the answer as
   a. true if the item is an absolute statement.
   b. true if the item contains negative words or word parts.
   c. false if the item contains unfamiliar terminology.
   d. false if you have to take a guess.

_____ 5. When you are taking a matching test, you should do all of the following *except*
   a. choose the first answer you see that seems correct.
   b. try to discover a pattern.
   c. answer the items you are sure of first.
   d. get an overview of the subjects before you match any items.

_____ 6. On a multiple-choice test, you probably can rule out an answer that contains the qualifying word
   a. sometimes.
   b. usually.
   c. often.
   d. never.

_____ 7. On a standardized test, it is most important to
   a. take your time.
   b. finish the test.
   c. figure out the point distribution.
   d. work quickly but carefully.

_____ 8. In order to reduce test anxiety, you should try to do all of the following _except_
   a. become familiar with the testing location.
   b. avoid taking practice tests and make-up exams.
   c. control negative thinking.
   d. practice working within time limits.

_____ 9. The following question appears on an essay exam in history: "Discuss the social and economic consequences of the Industrial Revolution." In this example, the key word or phrase is
   a. "Discuss."
   b. "social and economic."
   c. "consequences."
   d. "Industrial Revolution."

_____ 10. One rule of thumb for writing effective answers on essay exams is to always
   a. leave the page blank if you don't know the answer.
   b. begin your answer with a thesis statement.
   c. include your personal reaction to the topic.
   d. present your answer in outline form.

CHAPTER 18
IMPROVING YOUR READING RATE AND FLEXIBILITY

Directions: *Write the letter of the choice that best completes each statement in the space provided.*

_____ 1. The most important thing to remember about your reading rate is that
   a. it should always be around 300 words per minute.
   b. it is never appropriate to skip words.
   c. you should be able to read at several speeds.
   d. prereading decreases your reading speed.

_____ 2. Although it is not considered a good habit, moving your lips as you read can often
   a. increase your reading rate dramatically.
   b. help you understand difficult or complicated material.
   c. indicate that you are a faster than average reader.
   d. help you keep your place on the page.

_____ 3. Ray is reading an article for his film class. If he were to divide the following sentence from the article into meaningful clusters, it would look like
   a. The anamorphic lens made possible / the horizontal widening of / the visual field.
   b. The anamorphic lens / made possible / the horizontal widening / of the visual field.
   c. The anamorphic lens / made possible the / horizontal widening of the / visual field.
   d. The anamorphic / lens made possible / the horizontal / widening of the visual field.

_____ 4. Lily has decided to try pacing as a way of improving her reading rate. This information indicates that she specifically plans to
   a. become familiar with the material's organization and content before she reads it.
   b. allow herself frequent regressions within the same paragraph.
   c. reread the same material several times, each time faster than the last.
   d. push herself to read faster than normal while maintaining her comprehension.

_____ 5. Your reading rate typically would be slowest for material such as
   a. poetry.
   b. newspapers.
   c. reference material.
   d. novels.

6. When you are learning to adjust your reading rate, it is *least* important to
   a. preread the material.
   b. develop flexibility.
   c. define your overall purpose for reading.
   d. figure out precisely how much to increase your speed.

7. Reading selectively is most appropriate for material that
   a. does not require a high level of comprehension.
   b. is unfamiliar.
   c. provides little or no background information.
   d. does not include any examples.

8. The purpose of scanning is to
   a. get an overall picture of the material.
   b. become generally familiar with the topics and ideas presented.
   c. search for specific information.
   d. make sure you understand the material.

9. Skim-reading refers to situations in which
   a. you plan to read the entire article or chapter more intensively later.
   b. skimming is the only coverage you plan to give the material.
   c. you are going back over material that you have already read.
   d. the introduction and the summary are all that you plan to read.

10. Your range of speed in words per minute should be slowest when your purpose for reading is
    a. analysis, evaluation, or critique.
    b. enjoyment or entertainment.
    c. overview of reference material.
    d. location of a specific fact.

ANSWER KEY TO CHAPTER REVIEW QUIZZES–TEST BANK 1

CHAPTER 1

1.	d	6.	d
2.	c	7.	a
3.	a	**8.**	b
4.	a	9.	c
5.	b	10.	c

CHAPTER 2

1.	a	6.	b
2.	c	7.	a
3.	d	**8.**	a
4.	c	9.	d
5.	b	10.	c

CHAPTER 3

1.	b	6.	b
2.	a	7.	a
3.	a	**8.**	c
4.	d	9.	c
5.	a	10.	b

CHAPTER 4

1.	d	6.	c
2.	b	7.	c
3.	b	**8.**	a
4.	d	9.	c
5.	b	10.	d

CHAPTER 5

1.	c	6.	b
2.	d	7.	d
3.	a	**8.**	c
4.	d	9.	c
5.	c	10.	b

CHAPTER 6

1.	a	6.	c
2.	c	7.	c
3.	a	8.	b
4.	a	9.	c
5.	c	10.	a

CHAPTER 7

1.	d	6.	a
2.	a	7.	b
3.	c	8.	a
4.	a	9.	c
5.	c	10.	a

CHAPTER 8

1.	c	6.	a
2.	c	7.	b
3.	a	8.	d
4.	b	9.	a
5.	a	10.	d

CHAPTER 9

1.	d	6.	b
2.	b	7.	c
3.	a	8.	d
4.	d	9.	b
5.	c	10.	c

CHAPTER 10

1.	d	6.	d
2.	c	7.	a
3.	d	8.	c
4.	a	9.	b
5.	d	10.	a

CHAPTER 11

1.	a	6.	b
2.	c	7.	d
3.	d	8.	a
4.	d	9.	d
5.	b	10.	d

CHAPTER 12

1.	d	6.	a
2.	a	7.	a
3.	d	8.	c
4.	b	9.	c
5.	c	10.	b

CHAPTER 13

1.	c	6.	d
2.	a	7.	c
3.	b	8.	d
4.	d	9.	d
5.	c	10.	a

CHAPTER 14

1.	c	6.	b
2.	b	7.	d
3.	d	8.	c
4.	a	9.	c
5.	c	10.	b

CHAPTER 15

1.	a	6.	c
2.	c	7.	b
3.	c	8.	c
4.	d	9.	c
5.	d	10.	b

CHAPTER 16

1.	a	6.	c
2.	b	7.	b
3.	c	8.	b
4.	d	9.	a
5.	d	10.	a

CHAPTER 17

1.	d	6.	d
2.	d	7.	d
3.	c	8.	b
4.	c	9.	a
5.	a	10.	b

CHAPTER 18

1.	c	6.	d
2.	b	7.	a
3.	b	8.	c
4.	d	9.	b
5.	a	10.	a

PART TWO

CHAPTER REVIEW QUIZZES—TEST BANK 2

CHAPTER 1
SETTING GOALS AND MANAGING YOUR TIME

Directions: *Write the letter of the choice that best completes each statement in the space provided.*

_____ 1. For every hour spent in class, most instructors expect you to study for
   a. 15 minutes.
   b. 30 minutes.
   c. 1 hour.
   d. 2 hours.

_____ 2. An example of a well-defined goal is
   a. "I want to earn a million dollars a year."
   b. "I don't want to have to worry about paying my bills."
   c. "I want to earn a bachelor's degree in fine arts within four years."
   d. "I want to win the Nobel Peace Prize."

_____ 3. A term plan should include all of the following *except*
   a. class hours.
   b. family obligations.
   c. meals.
   d. social activities.

_____ 4. The primary purpose of your weekly schedule is to show
   a. long-standing commitments.
   b. priorities and goals.
   c. specific times for studying and completing assignments.
   d. time spent outside of class.

_____ 5. The best strategy for studying is to
   a. take on difficult subjects first.
   b. get easy assignments out of the way early in the evening.
   c. schedule one long, uninterrupted block of time for each subject.
   d. take an hour-long break after each hour of studying.

_____ 6. For a class that meets on Thursday morning, you should plan to study on
   a. Monday evening.
   b. Tuesday morning.
   c. Wednesday evening.
   d. Saturday morning.

43

_____ 7. All of the following are effective time-saving techniques *except*
a. using spare time as study time.
b. using lists to keep yourself organized.
c. combining daily activities with class assignments.
d. making appointments in person rather than using the telephone.

_____ 8. The best way to overcome a tendency to procrastinate is to
a. spend time away from your desk taking care of errands.
b. leave the television on to help you relax while you are studying.
c. divide the task into shorter, more manageable parts.
d. avoid working on tasks that you are unsure about.

_____ 9. When you are creating your weekly schedule, you should
a. estimate the amount of time you will need for each course.
b. leave out minor appointments, such as getting a haircut or babysitting.
c. focus only on those assignments that are due during that particular week.
d. plan to study subjects one right after another, without any breaks.

_____ 10. Of the following tasks, the best one to work on later in the evening is
a. studying for the final exam in a difficult biology class.
b. learning a new and complicated accounting method.
c. copying statistical formulas from a textbook onto index cards.
d. reading and highlighting a chapter in an economics textbook.

CHAPTER 2
LEARNING STYLE AND LEARNING STRATEGIES

Directions: *Write the letter of the choice that best completes each statement in the space provided.*

_____ 1. Your learning style refers to the
a. methods and strategies you use to learn.
b. amount of information you can remember.
c. types of tasks you are able to learn.
d. level of thinking you apply to situations.

_____ 2. The auditory/visual section of the Learning Style Questionnaire indicates
a. the types of learning tasks and learning situations you find easiest to handle.
b. the sensory mode you prefer when processing information.
c. your ability to work with spatial relationships.
d. your preferred level of interaction with other people.

_____ 3. The learning strategy that would be most appropriate for both visual and spatial learners would involve
a. drawing diagrams, charts, and maps.
b. tape-recording lectures.
c. writing summaries.
d. talking aloud when studying.

_____ 4. Once you identify your learning style, you should do all of the following *except*
a. accept your style as fixed and unchanging.
b. work on improving any areas of weakness.
c. take advantage of your strengths.
d. adjust your learning style to accommodate your instructors' teaching styles.

_____ 5. Learning in college is different from high school in that college instructors
a. place more emphasis on reviews of factual course content.
b. focus on "right answers" rather than ideas.
c. spend more time providing drills and practice lessons.
d. expect students to take responsibility for their own learning.

_____ 6. Active learners are characterized by all of the following learning strategies *except*
   a. asking questions while reading textbook assignments.
   b. considering the purpose behind assignments.
   c. predicting what questions will appear on exams.
   d. doing only what is expected to get a good grade.

_____ 7. According to the progression of thinking skills developed by Benjamin Bloom, the highest level of thinking is
   a. knowledge.
   b. comprehension.
   c. evaluation.
   d. application.

_____ 8. Memorizing definitions for a history exam is an example of an assignment at the
   a. knowledge level.
   b. application level.
   c. analysis level.
   d. synthesis level.

_____ 9. Writing an original poem in the style of Emily Dickinson is an example of an assignment at the
   a. knowledge level.
   b. analysis level.
   c. synthesis level.
   d. evaluation level.

_____ 10. Writing an assessment of a classmate's presentation in a public speaking class is an example of an assignment at the
   a. comprehension level.
   b. application level.
   c. synthesis level.
   d. evaluation level.

CHAPTER 3
UNDERSTANDING HOW LEARNING AND MEMORY WORK

Directions: *Write the letter of the choice that best completes each statement in the space provided.*

_____ 1. According to the retention curve, the amount of learned information that most people can recall after an hour is about
  a. 90 percent.
  b. 75 percent.
  c. 50 percent.
  d. 25 percent.

_____ 2. Encoding is the process by which information
  a. enters the brain.
  b. is stored in memory.
  c. is transferred into long-term memory.
  d. is discarded.

_____ 3. The function of sensory storage is to
  a. hold information while the brain interprets it.
  b. make new information fit with existing information.
  c. retrieve information from long-term memory.
  d. store new information indefinitely.

_____ 4. Information remains in short-term memory for
  a. less than a minute.
  b. about 10 minutes.
  c. about an hour.
  d. at least a day.

_____ 5. The Number Seven Theory states that short-term memory is limited to seven
  a. single items at a time.
  b. sets of information at a time.
  c. days' worth of information.
  d. minutes' worth of information at a time.

_____ 6. All of the following are effective strategies for improving storage of information *except*
   a. reviewing your notes immediately after a lecture.
   b. using mnemonic devices.
   c. organizing information into groups or sets.
   d. studying a chapter by rereading it.

_____ 7. Connecting a marketing assignment with a personal experience is an example of
   a. elaborative rehearsal.
   b. rote learning.
   c. recoding.
   d. retrieval.

_____ 8. Memorizing the exact definition of a word is an example of
   a. elaborative rehearsal.
   b. rote learning.
   c. recoding.
   d. retrieval.

_____ 9. Outlining a reading assignment is an example of
   a. elaborative rehearsal.
   b. rote learning.
   c. recoding.
   d. retrieval.

_____ 10. Solving a math problem on an exam is an example of
   a. elaborative rehearsal.
   b. rote learning.
   c. recoding.
   d. retrieval.

CHAPTER 4
TAKING NOTES IN CLASS

Directions: *Write the letter of the choice that best completes each statement in the space provided.*

_____ 1. The average adult spends most of each waking hour
a. speaking.
b. writing.
c. listening.
d. reading.

_____ 2. Listening can be described as all of the following *except*
a. intellectual.
b. intentional.
c. purposeful.
d. passive.

_____ 3. Compared to the average rate of speech, the rate at which you can process ideas is
a. slightly slower.
b. much slower.
c. much faster.
d. about the same.

_____ 4. In order to sharpen your listening skills during a lecture, you should focus on all of the following *except*
a. main ideas.
b. significant trends.
c. the speaker's delivery.
d. patterns of thought.

_____ 5. The most effective way to prepare for a lecture class would be to
a. review your notes from the previous lecture.
b. begin a reading assignment for another class.
c. discuss your homework with a classmate.
d. relax and let the topic of the lecture be a surprise.

_____ 6. A good set of lecture notes should include all of the following *except*
a. the lecture's main points.
b. every detail and example given by the speaker.
c. the relative importance of ideas presented.
d. the organization of the lecture.

7. Speakers show what is important in a lecture in all of the following ways *except*
   a. listing and numbering points.
   b. writing information on overhead projectors or chalkboards.
   c. changing the tone or pitch of their voices.
   d. maintaining the same rate of speech.

8. The indentation system of organizing lecture notes is most similar to
   a. an outline.
   b. a diagram.
   c. a paragraph.
   d. a list.

9. One way to make note taking easier during a lecture is to
   a. sit near the back of the classroom.
   b. leave space to fill in any missing information later.
   c. plan to recopy your notes later.
   d. write your notes in pencil on small note cards.

10. In the recall clue system, the recall clues should be
    a. detailed examples that illustrate specific ideas in a lecture.
    b. abbreviations and symbols that represent frequently used words or phrases.
    c. page references of textbook passages that correspond to lecture material.
    d. words or questions that trigger your memory and help you recall information.

CHAPTER 5
ACTIVE READING STRATEGIES

Directions: *Write the letter of the choice that best completes each statement in the space provided.*

_____ 1. The overall purposes of prereading are to identify the most important ideas in the material and to
    a. form an opinion about the material.
    b. note the organization of the material.
    c. evaluate the author's writing style.
    d. verify specific facts and details in the material.

_____ 2. The first sentence under each heading in a chapter frequently provides the author's
    a. point of view.
    b. purpose.
    c. references.
    d. central thought.

_____ 3. The subtitle of a chapter indicates
    a. what new terms will be introduced in the chapter.
    b. what key points will be covered in the chapter.
    c. how the author will approach the overall topic.
    d. why the author is qualified to write about the topic.

_____ 4. Of the following types of material, prereading would be most useful for
    a. research reports.
    b. short stories.
    c. poetry.
    d. novels.

_____ 5. All of the following statements about making predictions are true *except*
    a. predicting forces the reader to work at higher levels of thinking.
    b. predictions should be made only about content, not organization.
    c. the process of making predictions occurs both before and during reading.
    d. efficient readers confirm, reject, or revise their predictions while reading.

6. Before reading the social responsibility chapter in her business textbook, Aimee free-associated about the topic, which means that she
   a. researched the topic in other textbooks.
   b. asked herself what she hoped to learn about the topic.
   c. interviewed experts in the field of social responsibility.
   d. made a list of everything she already knew about social responsibility.

7. The most effective guide questions are those that
   a. begin with *Who, When,* or *Where.*
   b. can be answered through superficial reading.
   c. require in-depth thought and detailed answers.
   d. lead to factual, one-word answers.

8. All of the following strategies can help you strengthen your comprehension *except*
   a. rephrasing each paragraph in your own words.
   b. rereading difficult or complicated sections.
   c. increasing your reading rate.
   d. highlighting key ideas.

9. The primary purpose of checkpoints is to allow you to
   a. evaluate your level of comprehension.
   b. outline important points.
   c. review material you have already read.
   d. discover relationships between topics.

10. The best example of internal dialogue is
    a. rewriting an assignment after getting feedback from the instructor.
    b. mentally outlining the steps to solving a math problem.
    c. rereading a chapter to make sure your notes were accurate.
    d. meeting with a study group to review for an exam.

CHAPTER 6
UNDERSTANDING PARAGRAPHS

Directions: *Write the letter of the choice that best completes each statement in the space provided.*

_____   1.   A paragraph can be defined as a
a.   collection of facts.
b.   group of related sentences.
c.   set of examples.
d.   writer's opinion.

_____   2.   The purpose of most of the sentences in a paragraph is to
a.   restate the topic sentence.
b.   provide examples.
c.   introduce new ideas.
d.   explain the main idea.

_____   3.   The topic sentence in a paragraph is usually the
a.   first sentence.
b.   second sentence.
c.   last sentence.
d.   first and last sentence.

_____   4.   To find the main idea of a paragraph, you should ask yourself the question:
a.   "What kinds of details does the author use to support the main idea?"
b.   "What is the author trying to say about the topic?"
c.   "What do I already know about the topic?"
d.   "How does the author feel about the topic?"

_____   5.   An author who uses an inductive thought pattern in a paragraph typically
a.   states the main idea at the beginning of the paragraph.
b.   states the main idea in the middle of the paragraph.
c.   builds up to the main idea and states it at the end of the paragraph.
d.   hints at the main idea but does not state it anywhere in the paragraph.

6. A paragraph has this topic sentence: "The Amazon rainforest is home to the richest variety of wildlife on Earth." Of the following details, the only one that would *not* belong in this paragraph is
   a. "Many unusual species, such as the emerald tree boa and the jaguar, can be found in the rainforest."
   b. "Numerous species of birds are found in the rain forest."
   c. "One of the largest marshland areas in the world is found in the Florida Everglades."
   d. "Piranhas and harpy eagles are two of the most lethal inhabitants of the rainforest."

7. The three essential elements of a paragraph are its topic, its main idea, and its
   a. topic sentence.
   b. transitions.
   c. supporting details.
   d. examples.

8. The phrase "for instance" is an example of the type of transition known as
   a. example.
   b. comparison.
   c. cause-effect.
   d. summation.

9. The phrase "in addition" is an example of the type of transition known as
   a. example.
   b. continuation.
   c. contrast.
   d. cause-effect.

10. The phrase "to conclude" is an example of the type of transition known as
   a. comparison.
   b. time-sequence.
   c. summation.
   d. enumeration.

CHAPTER 7
FOLLOWING THOUGHT PATTERNS

Directions: *Write the letter of the choice that best completes each statement in the space provided.*

_____ 1. In most textbooks, the progression of ideas typically goes from
  a. small to large.
  b. general to particular.
  c. limited to comprehensive.
  d. opinion to fact.

_____ 2. The thesis statement of an article or essay is usually presented in the
  a. introduction.
  b. body.
  c. conclusion.
  d. summary.

_____ 3. The type of supporting information that is used to show how a principle can be applied in a real situation consists of
  a. statistics.
  b. examples.
  c. reasons.
  d. research.

_____ 4. The primary purpose of a description is to
  a. explain why the writer supports a belief or action.
  b. lend support for a particular viewpoint.
  c. make an idea practical and understandable.
  d. help the reader create a mental picture.

_____ 5. Typically, the first part of a term's definition provides
  a. the general class or group that the term belongs to.
  b. distinguishing characteristics of the term.
  c. applications or examples describing the term.
  d. the appropriate context for the term.

_____ 6. The directional phrase typically associated with the definition thought pattern is
       a. as a result.
       b. refers to.
       c. in spite of.
       d. in addition.

Directions: *For each of the following topic sentences, write the letter of the choice that indicates the thought pattern most likely to be used throughout the remainder of the paragraph.*

_____ 7. A person accused of a crime may pass through six stages in the American criminal justice system.
       a. cause-effect
       b. problem-solution
       c. time sequence
       d. definition

_____ 8. High blood pressure has been associated with a variety of risk factors.
       a. cause-effect
       b. comparison-contrast
       c. time sequence
       d. definition

_____ 9. The Mayan pyramids were like the Egyptian pyramids in several ways.
       a. problem-solution
       b. cause-effect
       c. time sequence
       d. comparison-contrast

_____ 10. People identify their territory with three types of markers.
       a. definition
       b. enumeration
       c. problem-solution
       d. cause-effect

CHAPTER 8
READING GRAPHICS AND TECHNICAL WRITING

Directions: *Write the letter of the choice that best completes each statement in the space provided.*

_____ 1. In general, graphics are intended to do all of the following *except*
   a. condense and organize information.
   b. make complicated information easier to understand and retain.
   c. replace the corresponding text material.
   d. display trends and patterns in a clear form.

_____ 2. The purpose of a table is to
   a. depict relationships between quantities or amounts.
   b. present large amounts of information in a condensed form.
   c. show changes that occur with passing time.
   d. display the relative size or importance of various parts of a whole.

_____ 3. Your first step in studying a table should be to
   a. look for trends or patterns.
   b. make comparisons between variables.
   c. draw conclusions about the data.
   d. determine how the data are classified.

_____ 4. A linear graph showing the relationship between age and participation in volunteer activities indicated that, as age increased, participation in volunteer activities also increased. The relationship in this graph can be described as
   a. positive.
   b. independent.
   c. negative.
   d. inverse.

_____ 5. The most appropriate graphic for showing the process by which a bill becomes a law would be
   a. a pie chart.
   b. an organizational chart.
   c. a flowchart.
   d. a pictogram.

6. The most appropriate graphic for showing the percentages of deaths from different types of cancer would be
   a. a pie chart.
   b. an organizational chart.
   c. a flowchart.
   d. a pictogram.

7. The most appropriate graphic for showing the levels of the executive branch of government, from the president on down, would be
   a. a pie chart.
   b. an organizational chart.
   c. a flowchart.
   d. a pictogram.

8. Reading diagrams differs from reading other types of graphics because diagrams
   a. are intended primarily to elicit an emotional response.
   b. require the reader to refer frequently to the corresponding text.
   c. rely on symbols to make statistics seem realistic.
   d. are typically used in place of words to present information.

9. The best way to identify the symbols or codes used on a map is by looking at its
   a. caption.
   b. legend or key.
   c. distance scale.
   d. axes.

10. One characteristic of technical writing is that it
    a. contains very few graphics.
    b. avoids introducing specialized vocabulary.
    c. is used only in traditional technical or scientific fields.
    d. presents a large amount of facts as compactly as possible.

CHAPTER 9
READING AND EVALUATING ELECTRONIC SOURCES

Directions: *Write the letter of the choice that best completes each statement in the space provided.*

_____ 1. The Internet can be defined as a
a. collection of related Web pages linked together.
b. location on the Web where you can obtain information on a specific subject.
c. worldwide network of computers through which you can access a variety of information and services.
d. system of servers that allow the exchange of information through specially formatted documents.

_____ 2. All of the following are reasons why you should learn to use the Internet *except*
a. it is always the most reliable source of information.
b. instructors often expect students to use it to supplement their textbooks.
c. some sources of information are available only online.
d. it often provides more current information than traditional sources.

_____ 3. The best type of search tool to use when you are looking for a specific or obscure topic is a
a. subject directory.
b. search engine.
c. metasearch engine.
d. multi-task engine.

_____ 4. A Web site whose purpose is to promote products or services would most likely have an address ending in
a. edu.
b. gov.
c. com.
d. org.

_____ 5. The sponsor of a Web site is the person or organization who
a. designed the site.
b. provided the links to related sites.
c. wrote the material included on the site.
d. paid for the site to be created and placed on the Web.

6. A credible Web site should include all of the following *except*
   a. the date on which the site was last revised.
   b. working links to related sites.
   c. the author's professional credentials and/or contact information.
   d. the e-mail addresses of people who have visited the site.

7. All of the following are characteristic of electronic text *except* that it
   a. does not depend on other pages for meaning.
   b. is multidirectional rather than linear.
   c. comes in a wider variety of formats than traditional text.
   d. always follows the traditional organization of print paragraphs.

8. The primary purpose of bookmarking is to allow you to
   a. backtrack or retrace the links you followed in a search.
   b. record Web site addresses so you can access them easily later.
   c. search for a different Web site on a related topic.
   d. highlight a section of electronic text.

9. When you are visiting a Web site, it is most important to
   a. concentrate on the words and ignore the graphics.
   b. scroll down to see the next page.
   c. follow as many links as possible.
   d. focus on your purpose for visiting the site.

10. All of the following constitute plagiarism *except*
    a. copying and pasting directly from a Web site into your paper.
    b. using another person's exact words without enclosing them in quotation marks.
    c. using commonly known facts or information without citing a source.
    d. paraphrasing another person's words without giving credit to that person.

CHAPTER 10
CRITICAL THINKING AND READING

Directions: *Write the letter of the choice that best completes each statement in the space provided.*

_____ 1. An inference can best be described as
   a. an opinion.
   b. a true statement.
   c. a generalization.
   d. a reasoned guess.

_____ 2. Before you can make inferences about written material, you must
   a. be familiar with the topic.
   b. understand the literal meaning.
   c. decide how you feel about the topic.
   d. be able to verify your inferences in another source.

_____ 3. A critical mind-set is developed by asking all of the following questions *except*
   a. What is the source of the material?
   b. What are the author's qualifications?
   c. What is the author's purpose?
   d. What is the topic of the material?

_____ 4. Of the following sources of information for a research paper on the long-term effects of sun tanning, the most appropriate one would be
   a. an article in a fashion magazine.
   b. a brochure distributed by a tanning salon.
   c. an advertisement for alternative tanning supplies, such as pills and lotions.
   d. a Web site sponsored by the American Academy of Dermatology.

_____ 5. Of the following statements, the only one that is a fact is
   a. Frank Lloyd Wright was the greatest architect of all time.
   b. The Taj Mahal is a truly spectacular example of Islamic architecture.
   c. Michelangelo painted the ceiling of the Sistine Chapel between 1508 and 1512.
   d. Visiting the cathedral of Notre Dame in Paris is an unforgettable experience.

6. Of the following essay titles, the one that is most likely intended to inform rather than persuade is
   a. "Testing Cosmetics on Animals is Wrong."
   b. "The Evolution of the National Park System."
   c. "The Importance of Investing with Your Conscience."
   d. "Learning to Live with a Salt-Free Diet."

7. One way an author may reveal his or her bias is by *not* including
   a. examples based on personal experience.
   b. emotional language.
   c. opposing viewpoints.
   d. descriptive language.

8. To identify an author's tone, you should pay particular attention to the author's
   a. qualifications.
   b. evidence and examples.
   c. main idea and supporting details.
   d. word choice and sentence pattern.

9. A successful argument is one that makes a claim about an issue and then
   a. paraphrases the issue.
   b. calls the audience to action.
   c. supports the claim with evidence.
   d. contradicts the claim with opposing evidence.

10. Your first step in reading an argument should be to
    a. evaluate the evidence.
    b. identify the issue.
    c. highlight key evidence.
    d. outline the argument.

CHAPTER 11
EXPANDING YOUR VOCABULARY

Directions: *Write the letter of the choice that best completes each statement in the space provided.*

_____ 1. Most people's vocabularies consist of
   a. one level only.
   b. two levels, one for speaking and one for writing.
   c. two levels, one for reading and one for writing.
   d. four or more levels, each varying in strength.

_____ 2. Improving your vocabulary involves all of the following *except*
   a. reading a broad range of subjects and styles of writing.
   b. learning and using new words in your speech and writing.
   c. substituting long words for short words.
   d. replacing overused words with more precise, expressive words.

_____ 3. The most information on each word in the English language can be found in
   a. a standard desk dictionary.
   b. a subject area dictionary.
   c. a collegiate edition desk dictionary.
   d. an unabridged dictionary.

_____ 4. Compared to a desk dictionary, a pocket dictionary is more
   a. expensive.
   b. inclusive.
   c. convenient.
   d. extensive.

_____ 5. A thesaurus is the best place to look for a word's
   a. definition.
   b. synonyms.
   c. origin.
   d. pronunciation.

6. The glossary of a textbook is a
   a. new-terms list at the beginning of each chapter.
   b. set of review questions at the end of each chapter.
   c. list of references at the end of the book.
   d. comprehensive list of terms at the end of the book.

7. The most important step in learning specialized terminology is to
   a. recognize the difference between common terms and technical terms.
   b. familiarize yourself with the everyday meanings of technical terms.
   c. develop a systematic way of identifying, recording, and learning new terms.
   d. use the glossary to test your understanding of new terms.

8. When specialized terminology is introduced during a lecture, you should
   a. immediately locate the definition in your text.
   b. ignore the term if you are unfamiliar with it.
   c. record it in the margin of your textbook.
   d. distinguish the term and its definition from other facts in your notes.

9. When you use the vocabulary card system for new terminology, you should include all of the following information about a word on each card *except*
   a. its meaning.
   b. a guide to its pronunciation.
   c. other, similar words and their definitions.
   d. an example of how it is used.

10. The vocabulary card system is effective for all of the following reasons *except*
    a. you are forced to learn the words in a fixed order.
    b. you can review the cards in your spare time.
    c. words you know can be separated from words you don't know.
    d. you can review all the words periodically to refresh your memory.

CHAPTER 12
USING CONTEXT AND WORD PARTS

Directions: *Write the letter of the choice that best completes each statement in the space provided.*

_____ 1. If pronouncing an unfamiliar word aloud does not help you figure out its meaning, your next step should be to
   a. look it up in a dictionary.
   b. refer to a thesaurus.
   c. analyze its prefix, root, and suffix.
   d. look for context clues in the sentence or paragraph.

_____ 2. An astronomy class syllabus included this statement: "We will study tectonics–the internal forces that act to create surface features–during our unit on planetary geology." The type of context clue in the syllabus is
   a. a definition.
   b. an example.
   c. an illustration.
   d. a contrast.

_____ 3. The phrase that signals a contrast context clue is
   a. such as.
   b. on the other hand.
   c. for instance.
   d. to illustrate.

_____ 4. When you are learning word parts, you should remember that a
   a. word must have at least one prefix and one suffix.
   b. suffix always changes the spelling of the root word.
   c. prefix does not alter the meaning of the root word.
   d. word can have more than one prefix or suffix.

Directions: *Each of the following sentences contains a word whose meaning can be determined from the context. Select the choice that most clearly states the meaning of the underlined word as it is used in the sentence.*

_____ 5. Because of the sensational nature of the crime, the jury was <u>sequestered</u> until the trial was over.
   a. interviewed
   b. harassed
   c. isolated
   d. ignored

_____ 6. At first, the politician boasted that he had a spotless record, but he later admitted to some youthful <u>pecadillos</u>.
   a. mistakes
   b. ancestors
   c. profits
   d. activities

_____ 7. When a rainbow appeared over the church, it was considered an <u>auspicious</u> sign for the newly married couple.
   a. distracting
   b. lucky
   c. suspicious
   d. useful

Directions: *Each of the following words contains a root and a prefix and/or suffix. Using your knowledge of roots, prefixes, and suffixes, choose the best definition for each word.*

_____ 8. retrospective
   a. listening from a distance
   b. looking ahead
   c. looking backward
   d. turning away

_____ 9. contravene
   a. come toward
   b. send away
   c. cross over
   d. act against

_____ 10. audiology
   a. the quality of light
   b. the measurement of time
   c. the condition of vision
   d. the study of hearing

CHAPTER 13
TEXTBOOK HIGHLIGHTING AND MARKING

Directions: *Write the letter of the choice that best completes each statement in the space provided.*

_____ 1. Highlighting helps you do all of the following *except*
   a. keep you physically active while you read.
   b. see the organization of facts and ideas.
   c. avoid having to review material.
   d. evaluate what you read.

_____ 2. When you are learning to highlight textbooks, you should
   a. read the material before highlighting it.
   b. always highlight complete sentences.
   c. skip over boldface headings.
   d. highlight main ideas only.

_____ 3. As a general rule, you should try to highlight
   a. most of the sentences on a page.
   b. no more than one-third of each page.
   c. one key word from each sentence on a page.
   d. only the headings on a page.

_____ 4. Effective highlighting is characterized by all of the following *except*
   a. an appropriate amount of highlighted information.
   b. an accurate reflection of the content of the material.
   c. a combination of several different systems of highlighting.
   d. highlighted information that is easy to review.

_____ 5. One reason to supplement your textbook highlighting with marking is to
   a. increase the time you spend reviewing.
   b. record your opinion of the material.
   c. evaluate your highlighting skills.
   d. show relationships between facts and ideas.

6. All of the following are good examples of marking *except*
   a. circling unfamiliar words.
   b. crossing out confusing passages.
   c. noting possible test questions.
   d. numbering lists of ideas or events.

7. When you are marking information in a textbook, it is most important to
   a. mark only the information that has not been highlighted.
   b. make sure someone else can understand your notes.
   c. find out what you already know about the topic.
   d. use the opportunity to operate at higher levels of thinking.

8. Summary notes are most effectively used in passages that
   a. contain long and complicated ideas.
   b. are presented in the conclusion of a chapter.
   c. are short and easy to understand.
   d. consist primarily of illustrations or graphics.

9. When you use summary notes, you should always
   a. copy the author's exact words.
   b. write notes in complete sentences.
   c. use words that will trigger your memory.
   d. highlight the material thoroughly first.

10. The *least* effective use of your study time would be to
    a. highlight important passages as you read.
    b. make summary notes in the margins of your textbook.
    c. mark definitions and examples in your textbook.
    d. reread an entire chapter after reading it once.

CHAPTER 14
METHODS OF ORGANIZING INFORMATION

Directions: *Write the letter of the choice that best completes each statement in the space provided.*

_____ 1. All of the following are methods of consolidating information *except*
   a. outlining.
   b. rereading.
   c. summarizing.
   d. mapping.

_____ 2. When you create an outline, your level of thinking involves
   a. comprehension only.
   b. analysis only.
   c. synthesis only.
   d. analysis and synthesis.

_____ 3. Outlining requires you to do all of the following *except*
   a. think about the material you read.
   b. recopy ideas and information directly from a book.
   c. sort out important ideas from those that are less important.
   d. show how ideas interconnect.

_____ 4. Using standard outline format, the item placed closest to the left margin would be
   a. a major topic.
   b. an important detail.
   c. a minor detail.
   d. an example.

_____ 5. The most important aspect of an effective outline is that
   a. it uses complete sentences.
   b. each idea is numbered or lettered correctly.
   c. all items fit exactly into the standard format.
   d. the information under each heading supports or explains it.

6. Outlining would be appropriate for all of the following situations *except*
   a. organizing information about the steps in treating head injuries.
   b. writing an evaluation of an essay on public education reform.
   c. reading and memorizing basic definitions on a vocabulary list.
   d. sorting information about types of plants in a botany textbook.

7. Compared to an outline, a summary is less
   a. factual.
   b. detailed.
   c. objective.
   d. condensed.

8. Before writing a summary, you should always
   a. identify key definitions.
   b. locate the author's main point.
   c. define your purpose.
   d. evaluate the details.

9. A summary should include all of the following information *except*
   a. the author's main idea.
   b. your analysis of the passage.
   c. key terms and definitions.
   d. important supporting information.

10. The most appropriate map for showing the key events in the Cold War would be a
   a. process diagram.
   b. time line.
   c. part/function diagram.
   d. comparison-contrast chart.

CHAPTER 15
STUDY AND REVIEW STRATEGIES

Directions: *Write the letter of the choice that best completes each statement in the space provided.*

_____ 1. Paraphrasing can be defined as
   a. quoting an author's exact words.
   b. restating an author's ideas in your own words.
   c. using the author's statements in a summary.
   d. changing the meaning of a passage.

_____ 2. Paraphrasing is most useful for working with material that
   a. is well-written.
   b. is easy to understand.
   c. uses simple, non-technical language.
   d. requires exact, detailed comprehension.

_____ 3. To paraphrase effectively, you should do all of the following *except*
   a. read slowly and carefully.
   b. read the material before writing anything.
   c. change the author's arrangement or order of ideas.
   d. work with ideas rather than word by word.

_____ 4. Self-testing is a study strategy that involves
   a. using old exams to figure out what will appear on a new exam.
   b. memorizing review questions at the end of a chapter.
   c. writing and answering possible test questions.
   d. taking an exam home to complete outside the classroom.

_____ 5. The most useful types of questions for self-testing are
   a. open-ended.
   b. true/false.
   c. multiple-choice.
   d. matching.

_____ 6. Of the following self-test questions, the one that requires the highest level of thinking is
   a. "When does *To Kill A Mockingbird* take place?"
   b. "Where was Harper Lee born?"
   c. "How old were the main characters in the story?"
   d. "How effectively does the author portray race relations in the South during the Depression?"

_____ 7. The purpose of a learning journal is to help you to
   a. keep track of reading assignments.
   b. record and evaluate learning techniques.
   c. organize your course materials.
   d. summarize difficult or lengthy passages.

_____ 8. The first step in the SQ3R system involves
   a. prereading.
   b. summarizing.
   c. paraphrasing.
   d. self-testing.

_____ 9. During the recite step of SQ3R, you should be
   a. forming questions that you can answer as you read.
   b. answering end-of-chapter questions.
   c. checking your recall for each section.
   d. reading each boldface heading aloud.

_____ 10. One popular modification of the SQ3R system is the addition of a fourth "R," which recognizes the importance of
   a. evaluating.
   b. reacting.
   c. rereading.
   d. writing.

CHAPTER 16
PREPARING FOR EXAMS

Directions: *Write the letter of the choice that best completes each statement in the space provided.*

_____ 1. One of the best ways to prepare for an exam is to
  a. simulate the test conditions.
  b. spend most of your time rereading the material.
  c. study new material right before the exam.
  d. skip class and use the time to study instead.

_____ 2. In preparing for an exam, you should do all of the following *except*
  a. review assigned textbook chapters.
  b. go over relevant lecture notes.
  c. memorize questions from old exams.
  d. talk with other students about the material.

_____ 3. If an instructor frequently asks application questions on exams, you should adjust your study methods to focus on
  a. facts, dates, and definitions.
  b. connections between and among topics.
  c. practical situations and uses.
  d. cause-effect relationships.

_____ 4. All of the following strategies will help you learn to synthesize information *except*
  a. looking for relationships among ideas.
  b. focusing only on facts and details.
  c. identifying patterns in class lectures.
  d. obtaining perspective on the course material.

_____ 5. To discover the progression of ideas in a textbook, you should study the
  a. preface.
  b. glossary.
  c. appendices.
  d. table of contents.

6. Of the following types of information, a study sheet would be *least* useful for reviewing
   a. complex events.
   b. controversial issues.
   c. trends in data.
   d. groups of unrelated facts.

7. Predicting essay questions at the evaluation level of thinking involves
   a. seeing relationships.
   b. pulling ideas together.
   c. assessing value.
   d. recalling facts.

8. The index card system is most appropriate for reviewing
   a. brief facts.
   b. concepts and theories.
   c. cause-effect relationships.
   d. sequences of events.

9. The index card system helps you do all of the following *except*
   a. study in your spare time.
   b. memorize information in a fixed order only.
   c. focus on what you do not know rather than what you have already learned.
   d. review regularly until you have learned all the information.

10. Your first step in preparing for an essay test should be to
    a. predict possible questions.
    b. outline possible answers.
    c. identify probable topics.
    d. create a list of key words.

CHAPTER 17
TAKING EXAMS

Directions: *Write the letter of the choice that best completes each statement in the space provided.*

_____ 1. All of the following are effective approaches to taking an exam *except*
  a. sitting in the front of the exam room.
  b. arriving at least a half hour before the exam begins.
  c. bringing the necessary material, including extra pens and paper.
  d. prereading the exam before answering any questions.

_____ 2. For an exam consisting of multiple-choice questions worth 45 points and an essay portion worth 55 points, you should plan to spend most of your time
  a. prereading the questions.
  b. answering the multiple-choice questions.
  c. answering the essay questions.
  d. reviewing your answers.

_____ 3. If you do not know the answer to a question on an objective exam, you should
  a. leave the question blank.
  b. circle the question number but leave it blank.
  c. fill in your best guess and return to the question later.
  d. fill in your two best guesses and return to the question later.

_____ 4. All of the following are examples of limiting words in true/false statements *except*
  a. never.
  b. always.
  c. some.
  d. because.

_____ 5. When you are trying to answer a difficult true/false question, you should mark as false any items that contain
  a. two or more parts.
  b. negative words.
  c. unfamiliar terminology.
  d. comparisons between two items.

6. When you are taking a matching test, you should do all of the following *except*
   a. get an overview of the subjects before answering any items.
   b. try to discover a pattern to what is being matched.
   c. choose the first answer that seems correct.
   d. answer the items you are sure of first.

7. To improve your success on multiple-choice tests, you should
   a. always choose the shortest answer.
   b. answer the item first in your own words.
   c. eliminate choices that seem similar.
   d. select answers that use difficult words.

8. On a standardized test, you should expect to
   a. get most of the answers correct.
   b. work at a fairly rapid rate.
   c. finish the test in the allotted time.
   d. be penalized for guessing.

9. In the essay question, "Evaluate the strategies our justice system has used to deal with youthful offenders," the key word or phrase is
   a. "Evaluate."
   b. "the strategies."
   c. "our justice system."
   d. "youthful offenders."

10. An effective answer to an essay question includes all of the following *except*
    a. a thesis statement.
    b. your personal reaction to the topic.
    c. sufficient explanation or support.
    d. complete, correct sentences.

CHAPTER 18
IMPROVING YOUR READING RATE AND FLEXIBILITY

Directions: *Write the letter of the choice that best completes each statement in the space provided.*

_____ 1. One characteristic of good readers is that they
  a. read every assignment the same way.
  b. are able to read at different rates.
  c. never skip words.
  d. always read around 400 words per minute.

_____ 2. A reading habit that may help you understand difficult material is moving your
  a. lips or whispering aloud as you read.
  b. head rather than just your eyes as you read.
  c. thumb down the margin as a guide to where you are on the page.
  d. eyes backward to a word in the same line or in a line already read.

_____ 3. Of the following sentences, the one that is divided into meaningful clusters is
  a. A physically active lifestyle / is essential to improving cardiovascular health.
  b. A / physically active / lifestyle / is essential / to improving / cardiovascular / health.
  c. A physically active lifestyle/ is essential to improving / cardiovascular health.
  d. A / physically / active / lifestyle is essential / to improving / cardiovascular / health.

_____ 4. The technique of pacing involves
  a. predicting what an author will say about a topic.
  b. rereading material several times, each time faster than the last.
  c. assessing the difficulty of both the writing style and the content of the material.
  d. reading faster than normal while maintaining your level of comprehension.

_____ 5. Your reading rate would be slowest when your purpose for reading is to
  a. gain an overview of reference material.
  b. locate a specific fact in a textbook.
  c. analyze and evaluate a poem.
  d. enjoy an entertaining magazine article.

_____ 6. Reading selectively is appropriate for when you are
    a. expected to recall most of the facts and details in the material.
    b. searching for specific information.
    c. unfamiliar with what you are reading.
    d. not interested in the material.

_____ 7. Skimming is similar to the technique of
    a. prereading.
    b. outlining.
    c. mapping.
    d. paraphrasing.

_____ 8. Skim-reading refers to situations in which you
    a. intend to read the material more intensively later.
    b. have already read the material and are reviewing it.
    c. do not plan to give the material any further coverage.
    d. read the introduction and the summary only.

_____ 9. The purpose of skimming is to
    a. locate the answer to a question.
    b. find a particular piece of information.
    c. get an overall picture of the material.
    d. make sure you understand difficult material.

_____ 10. The purpose of scanning is to
    a. locate the answer to a question.
    b. become familiar with topics and main ideas.
    c. obtain an overview of the material.
    d. be sure you understand the material.

ANSWER KEY TO CHAPTER REVIEW QUIZZES–TEST BANK 2

CHAPTER 1

1.	d	6.	c
2.	c	7.	d
3.	d	8.	c
4.	c	9.	a
5.	a	10.	c

CHAPTER 2

1.	a	6.	d
2.	b	7.	c
3.	a	8.	a
4.	a	9.	c
5.	d	10.	d

CHAPTER 3

1.	c	6.	d
2.	a	7.	a
3.	a	8.	b
4.	a	9.	c
5.	b	10.	d

CHAPTER 4

1.	c	6.	b
2.	d	7.	d
3.	c	8.	a
4.	d	9.	b
5.	a	10.	d

CHAPTER 5

1.	b	6.	d
2.	d	7.	c
3.	c	8.	c
4.	a	9.	a
5.	b	10.	b

CHAPTER 6

1.	b	6.	c
2.	d	7.	c
3.	a	8.	a
4.	b	9.	b
5.	c	10.	c

CHAPTER 7

1.	b	6.	b
2.	a	7.	c
3.	b	8.	a
4.	d	9.	d
5.	a	10.	b

CHAPTER 8

1.	c	6.	a
2.	b	7.	b
3.	d	8.	b
4.	a	9.	b
5.	c	10.	d

CHAPTER 9

1.	c	6.	d
2.	a	7.	d
3.	c	8.	b
4.	c	9.	c
5.	d	10.	c

CHAPTER 10

1.	d	6.	b
2.	b	7.	c
3.	d	8.	d
4.	d	9.	c
5.	c	10.	b

CHAPTER 11

1.	d	6.	d
2.	c	7.	c
3.	d	8.	d
4.	c	9.	c
5.	b	10.	a

CHAPTER 12

1.	d	6.	a
2.	a	7.	b
3.	b	8.	c
4.	d	9.	d
5.	c	10.	d

CHAPTER 13

1.	c	6.	b
2.	a	7.	d
3.	b	8.	a
4.	c	9.	d
5.	d	10.	d

CHAPTER 14

1.	b	6.	c
2.	d	7.	b
3.	b	8.	c
4.	a	9.	b
5.	d	10.	b

CHAPTER 15

1.	b	6.	d
2.	d	7.	b
3.	c	8.	a
4.	c	9.	c
5.	a	10.	d

CHAPTER 16

1.	a	6.	d
2.	c	7.	c
3.	c	8.	a
4.	b	9.	b
5.	d	10.	c

CHAPTER 17

1.	b	6.	c
2.	c	7.	b
3.	c	8.	b
4.	d	9.	a
5.	c	10.	b

CHAPTER 18

1.	b	6.	b
2.	a	7.	a
3.	c	8.	c
4.	d	9.	c
5.	c	10.	a

PART THREE

MASTERY TESTS

CHAPTER 1
SETTING GOALS AND MANAGING YOUR TIME

Directions: *Read the following information and then answer questions 1-10.*

Jake is a sophomore majoring in physical therapy. He works part-time three days a week, and he also volunteers on Saturdays at a children's rehabilitation center. Listed below are the courses he is taking this term, as well as his course assignments for this week. Jake has partially completed his weekly schedule, which is shown on the next page.

COURSE	DAY & TIME
Biology	MWF 9-10
Biology Lab	TH 2-4
British Literature	MWF 11-12
Physical Therapy	T, TH 9:30-11
Motivational Psychology	MWF 2-3
Calculus	T, TH 12-1:30

COURSE	ASSIGNMENT
Biology	Read Chapters 5 and 6 in text; prepare for Friday's exam worth one-third of final grade
Biology Lab	Type one-page lab report (already written) due Thursday
British Literature	Read short story by Friday; alphabetize term paper bibliography due Wednesday
Physical Therapy	Read Chapter 2 in text; prepare and conduct interview with physical therapist
Motivational Psychology	Review Chapters 1-4; read psychology journal article and prepare analysis for discussion on Wednesday
Calculus	Do homework assignment for Tuesday; recopy formulas from text by Thursday

JAKE'S WORK AND STUDY SCHEDULE

	Monday	Tuesday	Wednesday	Thursday	Friday	Saturday	Sunday
7:00							
7:30							
8:00	Exercise	Exercise	Exercise	Exercise	Exercise		
8:30							
9:00	Biology		Biology		Biology		
9:30		P.T.		P.T.			
10:00			Copy A's				
10:30			Bio notes				
11:00	Brit. Lit	Lunch	Brit. Lit	Lunch	Brit. Lit		
11:30							
12:00	Lunch	Math	Lunch	Math	Lunch		
12:30							
1:00						Volunteer	
1:30							
2:00	Psych.	Call	Psych.	Biology	Psych.		
2:30		Library		lab			
3:00			Do				Work
3:30			Laundry				
4:00							
4:30							
5:00							
5:30							
6:00	Dinner	Dinner	Dinner	Dinner	Dinner		
6:30							
7:00		Work		Work	Go out w/		
7:30					friends		
8:00							
8:30							
9:00							

1. The first step Jake should take in creating his weekly schedule is to
    a. set his priorities and define his goals in specific, realistic terms.
    b. decide how much time he wants to set aside for social and leisure activities.
    c. choose the extracurricular activities he wants to participate in.
    d. reserve one day for studying and completing homework.

2. Based on the number of hours he spends in class each week, he should plan to study for about
    a. 5 hours.
    b. 8 hours.
    c. 17 hours.
    d. 34 hours.

3. Jake would make the best use of his time after his psychology class on Monday by
    a. taking a break until dinner.
    b. studying for his biology lab.
    c. reviewing his psychology lecture notes.
    d. exercising.

4. The assignment that he should work on earliest in his study session on Tuesday evening is
    a. alphabetizing his term paper bibliography for British literature.
    b. recopying math formulas for calculus.
    c. typing his biology lab report.
    d. reading and analyzing the psychology journal article.

5. One way that he could make the most effective use of his time on Wednesday is to
    a. read the short story assignment while he's doing his laundry.
    b. go to the library instead of calling to see if a book he requested is in.
    c. go to his British literature class early to chat with friends.
    d. copy his friend's biology notes by hand.

6. The best time for him to schedule study for his biology lab would be
    a. Monday morning.
    b. Tuesday afternoon.
    c. Wednesday evening.
    d. on the weekend.

7. The best way for him to prepare for his biology exam on Friday would be to
    a. skip class on Wednesday and use the time to study.
    b. plan to go over new material on Thursday evening.
    c. go out with friends on Thursday evening to relax before the exam.
    d. schedule time throughout the week to study and review the material.

8. While he is studying for his exam, he should plan to take a short break every
   a. 10 minutes.
   b. half hour.
   c. hour.
   d. 2 hours.

9. A physical therapist at the rehabilitation center has agreed to be interviewed for Jake's assignment, but Jake keeps procrastinating. All of the following suggestions could help him overcome his procrastination *except*
   a. making a list of questions he might ask.
   b. thinking positively about doing the interview.
   c. watching television while he writes possible interview questions.
   d. talking to his instructor about the best way to interview someone.

10. One way that Jake could make his schedule more effective on the weekend would be to
    a. pick up more work hours.
    b. designate time for study and review.
    c. volunteer on both Saturday and Sunday.
    d. extend his weekday exercise routine.

CHAPTER 2
LEARNING STYLE AND LEARNING STRATEGIES

Part I. Making the Most of Your Learning Style

Directions: Imagine that you are studying for an upcoming anatomy test. The test will cover four chapters. You will be expected to know the parts of the digestive system, how each part functions, and where each part is located. The exam will be somewhat detailed and will contain objective questions only.

To answer questions 1-10, refer to the scoring grid you completed after taking the Learning Style Questionnaire in Chapter 1. For each pair of questions below, choose the one question that reflects your profile on the questionnaire and answer that question only. For example, if your profile indicated that you are more visual than auditory, answer question 1. If your style is more conceptual than applied, answer question 4, and so on. For this section, you should answer five questions only.

Answer either 1 or 2:

1. If your learning style is VISUAL, the most suitable strategy for you would be to
   a. redraw parts of the digestive system.
   b. listen to audiotapes on the digestive system.
   c. join a study group where the digestive system is discussed in detail.
   d. translate diagrams into summaries.

2. If your learning style is AUDITORY, the most suitable strategy for you would be to
   a. draw a map of the digestive system.
   b. write possible test questions.
   c. tape-record lecture notes and listen to them again later.
   d. write the answers to discussion questions at the end of the chapter.

Answer either 3 or 4:

3. If your learning style is APPLIED, the most suitable strategy for you would be to
   a. review lecture notes by rereading them.
   b. listen to supplementary tapes on the digestive system.
   c. copy a blank picture of the digestive system and mark various parts.
   d. systematically reread each of the chapters.

4. If your learning style is CONCEPTUAL, the most suitable strategy for you would be to
    a. draw a diagram of the digestive system on paper.
    b. write a summary of how the digestive system works and how parts interact.
    c. create a map depicting the functions of the digestive system.
    d. draw the digestive system on the chalkboard and memorize it.

Answer either 5 or 6:

5. If your learning style is SPATIAL, the most suitable strategy for you would be to
    a. read lecture notes out loud to rehearse.
    b. paraphrase each of the assigned textbook chapters.
    c. write a brief summary on the functions of the digestive system.
    d. translate your lecture notes into a diagram.

6. If your learning style is NONSPATIAL, the most suitable strategy for you would be to
    a. draw a map of the digestive system and label the parts.
    b. review the functions of the digestive system by writing an outline.
    c. create a chart tracing the steps of the digestive system.
    d. depict the digestive system using pictures and symbols instead of words.

Answer either 7 or 8:

7. If your learning style is SOCIAL, the most suitable strategy for you would be to
    a. attend a group study session.
    b. study in a quiet atmosphere, taking frequent breaks.
    c. look up additional information in the library on your own.
    d. set the days and times you will study by yourself.

8. If your learning style is INDEPENDENT, the most suitable strategy for you would be to
    a. seek tutorial assistance.
    b. ask the instructor to organize a group study session.
    c. study in a quiet room in the library.
    d. discuss the important parts of each chapter with a friend.

Answer either 9 or 10:

9. If your learning style is CREATIVE, the most suitable strategy for you would be to
    a. answer the true/false questions at the end of each chapter.
    b. reread your notes and highlight key words.
    c. memorize a diagram of the digestive system.
    d. write possible test questions on each of the assigned chapters.

10. If your learning style is PRAGMATIC, the most suitable strategy for you would be to
   a. volunteer to "teach" a lesson on the part of the digestive system you already know.
   b. randomly draw a diagram on the digestive system, depicting each function with a different color.
   c. create a study plan in advance that outlines which subtopics you'll study on which days.
   d. write down all of the possible ways you could study the digestive system and do them all.

Part II. Identifying Levels of Thinking

Directions: *For questions 11-15, circle the letter that correctly identifies the highest level of thinking required for each task.*

11. Solving a simple algebraic equation.
   a. knowledge
   b. comprehension
   c. application
   d. evaluation

12. Listing three famous composers and their major works.
   a. knowledge
   b. application
   c. synthesis
   d. evaluation

13. Contrasting the platforms of two political candidates.
   a. knowledge
   b. comprehension
   c. application
   d. analysis

14. Explaining the definition of autism.
   a. comprehension
   b. analysis
   c. synthesis
   d. evaluation

15. Writing a poem in the style of Emily Dickinson.
   a. comprehension
   b. analysis
   c. synthesis
   d. evaluation

CHAPTER 3
UNDERSTANDING HOW LEARNING AND MEMORY WORK

Part I. The Memory Process

Directions: *For questions 1-5, circle the letter that correctly identifies whether the given task* <u>*primarily*</u> *involves encoding, storage, and/or retrieval.*

1. Taking an essay exam in art history.
   a. encoding
   b. storage
   c. retrieval
   d. encoding and storage

2. Listening to a lecture in botany without taking notes.
   a. encoding
   b. storage
   c. retrieval
   d. storage and retrieval

3. Solving a calculus problem.
   a. encoding
   b. storage
   c. retrieval
   d. encoding and retrieval

4. Taking notes on a video about public speaking.
   a. encoding
   b. storage
   c. retrieval
   d. encoding and storage

5. Writing an essay on the Spanish-American War.
   a. encoding
   b. storage
   c. retrieval
   d. encoding and retrieval

Part II. Storing Information

Directions: *For questions 6-7, circle the letter that correctly identifies how the information is stored for each task given.*

6. Memorizing the definition of the word <u>polyphony</u>.
    a. sensory storage
    b. rote learning
    c. elaborative rehearsal
    d. recoding

7. Taking notes in a political science lecture.
    a. sensory storage
    b. rote learning
    c. elaborative rehearsal
    d. recoding

Part III. Improving Storage and Retrieval

Directions: *For questions 8-10, circle the letter that corresponds to the best answer.*

8. The best way to use visualization to learn several important events and their dates for a history course is to
    a. tape-record the lectures containing events and dates.
    b. connect the events and dates using mnemonics.
    c. preread the chapter containing the information.
    d. make a chart or time line of the information.

9. The best way to use periodic review to study for a final exam covering several short stories studied in a modern fiction course would be to
    a. read each story twice in a row instead of just once.
    b. summarize the plots after reading each story and read the summaries weekly.
    c. draw a concept map for each story and study the map carefully before the exam.
    d. highlight and mark each story as you read it.

10. Assume that, for a botany exam, you must remember these three terms in order: vascular cambium, fronds, and phloem. You would be using a mnemonic device in this situation if you
    a. found out the Latin and/or Greek meanings of these words.
    b. drew a diagram of each of these terms illustrating their use.
    c. memorized the following sentence: Vaseline comes from petroleum.
    d. rehearsed the terms by continuous verbal and written repetition.

CHAPTER 4
TAKING NOTES IN CLASS

Directions: *Read the following situation and then answer questions 1-10.*

Charlie is taking a sociology class in which class lectures are very important. Although he typically finds the lectures interesting, he sometimes has difficulty taking notes, partly because his mind wanders and partly because he's not sure what's important to write down. He knows that he tends to have an applied learning style; that is, he prefers tasks that involve practical situations. Lately, he has been trying to get to class early so that he can get a good seat in hopes that it will improve his note taking.

1. For a good set of lecture notes, Charlie should make sure that he includes all of the following information *except*
    a. the lecture's main points.
    b. enough details so that he can recall the information later.
    c. his reactions to the ideas presented in the lecture.
    d. the organization of the lecture.

2. In order to sharpen his listening skills, he should
    a. focus on the lecturer's style of delivery.
    b. concentrate on recording facts rather than ideas.
    c. approach listening as an active rather than passive process.
    d. use the time during the lecturer's opening comments to get organized.

3. One reason that Charlie has time to think about other things during the lecture is probably because the average rate of speech is
    a. much faster than the speed of thought.
    b. much slower than the speed of thought.
    c. slightly slower than the speed of thought.
    d. much slower than the speed of writing.

4. Charlie's instructor would most likely indicate what is important to write down during the lecture is by doing any of the following *except*
    a. listing and numbering points.
    b. speaking faster.
    c. writing on the chalkboard.
    d. using audiovisual aids.

95

5. The best way for Charlie to organize his lecture notes would be by
   a. following the textbook's organization of the topic.
   b. grouping ideas in paragraph form.
   c. alphabetizing subtopics and supporting ideas.
   d. using an indentation system similar to outlining.

6. All of the following tips would help make his note taking more efficient *except*
   a. keeping a separate notebook for each course.
   b. tape-recording lectures and transcribing the notes later.
   c. abbreviating frequently used words.
   d. leaving blank space in his notes.

7. The best time for him to edit his lecture notes would be
   a. during the lecture.
   b. immediately after the lecture.
   c. later the same evening.
   d. several days later.

8. The most efficient way for him to review his notes is by
   a. reading his notes out loud.
   b. rereading his notes silently until he has them memorized.
   c. using the recall clue system to trigger his memory.
   d. exchanging his notes with those of a classmate.

9. Charlie can adapt his note taking to make the most of his learning style by
   a. thinking of practical examples and applications of the material.
   b. watching for patterns.
   c. studying with a classmate.
   d. translating diagrams and drawings into words.

10. In one lecture, Charlie's instructor focused on the nature of racism and described some local programs that attempt to improve race relations. In that lecture, the instructor most likely used the pattern known as
   a. comparison-contrast.
   b. problem-solution.
   c. classification.
   d. enumeration.

CHAPTER 5
ACTIVE READING STRATEGIES

Part I. Prereading and Predicting

Directions: *Read the following situation and then answer questions 1-5.*

Maggie is taking an American government course in which she has the following reading assignments: a newspaper article, a journal article, a textbook chapter titled "Civil Rights and Issues of Race," and a short story.

1. Of Maggie's reading assignments, prereading would be *least* appropriate for the
    a. newspaper article.
    b. journal article.
    c. textbook chapter.
    d. short story.

2. The main reason that Maggie should preread her assignments is to
    a. memorize facts and details.
    b. evaluate the author's qualifications.
    c. identify the most important ideas in the material.
    d. decide how she feels about the topic.

3. From the title of the textbook chapter, she can predict that the chapter will probably discuss all of the following topics *except*
    a. desegregation.
    b. feminism.
    c. voting rights.
    d. discrimination.

4. All of the following techniques would help her assess her comprehension of the journal article *except*
    a. free-associating.
    b. setting checkpoints.
    c. asking connection questions.
    d. using internal dialogue.

5. The *least* effective way for Maggie to strengthen her reading comprehension would be to
   a. read faster.
   b. highlight key ideas.
   c. reread complicated sections.
   d. read difficult sections aloud.

Part II. Forming Guide Questions

Directions: *Read the following textbook selection and then answer questions 6-10 identifying the best guide questions for each paragraph.*

GENETIC ENGINEERING

Genetic engineering, one of the most hotly disputed topics in science today, potentially has both appropriate and inappropriate applications. Our challenge as responsible, ethical members of society is to differentiate between the appropriate and inappropriate uses of this technology. **1**

Genetic engineering is the process in which genes, the fundamental physical units of heredity that transmit information from one cell to another, and hence one generation to another, are transferred from one organism to another. This is known as recombinant DNA technology. The genes are "cut" from the genetic material (deoxyribonucleic acid, or DNA) of one organism and "pasted" into the DNA of another. The organism that is most commonly used to receive the genes is the bacterium *Escherichia coli*. *E. coli* is used because its DNA structure is very simple compared to the DNA structure in plants or animals, and scientists understand this organism better than any other organism in the world. **2**

If the gene that has been inserted into the bacterium's DNA tells the bacterium's cell machinery to produce insulin, then it will produce insulin. Because bacteria grow and reproduce rapidly, large quantities of insulin will be produced. Genetically engineered bacteria are grown under controlled laboratory conditions because biologists believe that the bacteria are unable to live outside the laboratory. **3**

Biologists are now learning how to transfer genes into the DNA of plant cells. Unlike bacteria, which are one-celled organisms, plants are composed of millions of cells which perform specific functions, such as photosynthesis or new growth or reproduction. The DNA in plants is much more complicated than the DNA in bacteria. Because isolating a specific gene in a plant that codes for the production of a specific protein is difficult, scientists are using genetically altered bacteria to carry selected genes into plants.

4

Beneficial Uses of Biotechnology. Currently, products of genetic engineering are being developed that may prove beneficial to human health. Products that could benefit human health include insulin, used to treat diabetes; a human growth hormone used to treat dwarfism; factor VIII, a blood plasma protein that promotes clotting and is missing in the blood of hemophiliacs; tissue plasminogen activator, a blood protein that activates an enzyme that dissolves clots and may be useful in preventing strokes or heart attacks; interferon, an experimental antiviral, anticancer drug that was previously available in quantities too small for extensive clinical study; and vaccines, used to prevent currently incurable diseases such as herpes and rabies.

5

Potentially Destructive Uses of Biotechnology. In addition to its beneficial uses, genetic engineering can have unforeseen destructive effects on the environment. What if we release into the environment a genetically altered organism before we have fully studied its potential impact on the environment? While genetically altered bacteria generally cannot survive outside of the laboratory and into the environment, it could force us to change our fundamental view of nature. We can now create viable organisms outside of the normal course of evolution. What will be the effect on native plant and animal species if a genetically altered organism with no natural competitors is released in the environment? Could genetically engineered bacteria that feed on oil slicks enter the holds of tankers and destroy the cargo? Will plants that have been engineered to produce their own herbicides and pesticides be so successful at warding off weeds and insects that they become like weeds themselves, growing where they are not wanted?

6

—Kaufman and Franz, *Biosphere 2000*, pp. 561-63

6. The best guide question for the title of the selection would be
   a. What is genetic engineering?
   b. What are the different types of genetic engineering?
   c. Who were the first genetic engineers?
   d. Where did the first genetic engineering experiments take place?

7. The best guide question for paragraph 2, based on the first sentence, would be
   a. How is genetic engineering done?
   b. What organism do scientists understand better than any other organism in the world?
   c. What organism is most commonly used to receive genes?
   d. What does the abbreviation DNA stand for?

8. The best guide question for paragraph 4, based on the first sentence, would be
   a. Are bacteria one-celled organisms?
   b. Is the DNA in plants more complicated than the DNA in bacteria?
   c. What are three specific functions performed by plant cells?
   d. How are genes transferred into the DNA of plant cells?

9. The best guide question for the heading "Beneficial Uses of Biotechnology" would be
   a. How many beneficial uses are there?
   b. Who decides what is beneficial to whom?
   c. Where was biotechnology first used?
   d. How can biotechnology be used beneficially?

10. The best guide question for the heading "Potentially Destructive Uses of Biotechnology" would be
    a. What does destructive mean?
    b. How can biotechnology be used destructively?
    c. Is a potentially destructive use a realistic threat to the environment?
    d. By what standards is destructiveness determined?

CHAPTER 6
UNDERSTANDING PARAGRAPHS

Directions: *Read the following selection and then answer questions 1-10.*

PESTICIDES

Pesticides, of course, are products that kill pests. But biologically, the term "pest" has no meaning. The Colorado potato beetle, for example, was never regarded as a pest until it made its way (carried by humans) to Europe, where it began to interfere seriously with potato production. Perhaps this episode best illustrates a definition of a **pest**: it is something that interferes with humans. **1**

It seems that the greatest pesticidal efforts have been directed at insects and, clearly, much of it has been beneficial. The heavy application of DDT since World War II has caused sharp decreases in malaria and yellow fever in certain areas of the world. But DDT and other chlorinated hydrocarbons have continued to be spread indiscriminately any place in which insect pests are found. The result, of course, is a kind of–is it artificial or natural?–selection. The problem is that some insects had a bit more resistance to these chemicals than did others. These resistant ones then reproduced and, in turn, the most resistant of their offspring continued the line. The result is that we now have insects that can almost bathe in these chemicals without harm. **2**

There are also other risks involved in such wide use of insecticides. For example, most are unselective in their targets; they kill virtually *all* the insect species they contact. Many insects, of course, are beneficial and may form an important part of large ecosystems. Also, chemical insecticides move easily through the environment and can permeate far larger areas than intended. Another particularly serious problem with pesticides is that many of them persist in the environment for long periods. In other words, the chemicals are very stable and it is difficult for natural processes to break them down to their harmless components. Newer chemical pesticides are deadly in the short run, but quickly break down into harmless by-products. **3**

The tendency of DDT to be magnified in food chains has been particularly disastrous for predators that feed high on the food pyramid. This is because as one animal eats another in the food chain, the pesticide from each level is added to the next. Thus, species high on the food chain, the predators, tend to accumulate very high levels of these chemicals. In this light, recall that humans are often the top predator in food chains. The effects of accumulated DDT on predatory birds have been substantial. Reproductive failures in peregrine falcons, the brown pelican, and the Bermuda petrel have been attributed to ingesting high levels of DDT. The problem is that the pesticide interferes with the birds' ability to metabolize calcium. As a result, they lay eggs with shells too thin to support the weight of a nesting parent.

4

—Wallace, *Biology: The World of Life*, 6e, pp. 828-829

1. The topic of paragraph 1 is
    a. pests.
    b. pesticides.
    c. potato beetles.
    d. potato production.

2. In paragraph 1, the topic sentence begins with the word
    a. "Pesticides . . ."
    b. "But . . ."
    c. "The . . ."
    d. "Perhaps . . ."

3. The topic of paragraph 2 is
    a. World War II.
    b. chemical-resistant insects.
    c. DDT and other chlorinated hydrocarbons.
    d. malaria and yellow fever.

4. In paragraph 2, the topic sentence begins with the words
    a. "It seems . . ."
    b. "The problem is . . ."
    c. "These resistant ones . . ."
    d. "The result is . . ."

5. The main idea of paragraph 2 is that
    a. DDT continues to spread wherever insects are found.
    b. Most pesticides have been beneficial.
    c. Some insects have become immune to DDT.
    d. Only chemical-resistant insects continue to reproduce.

6. The topic of paragraph 3 is
    a. problems or risks of pesticides.
    b. large ecosystems.
    c. stable chemicals.
    d. harmless by-products.

7. In paragraph 3, the topic sentence begins with the words
    a. "There are . . ."
    b. "Many insects . . ."
    c. "Another particularly . . ."
    d. "Newer chemical . . ."

8. The topic of paragraph 4 is
    a. reproductive failures.
    b. the food pyramid.
    c. the effects of DDT.
    d. a bird's ability to metabolize calcium.

9. In paragraph 4, the topic sentence begins with the words
    a. "The tendency of . . ."
    b. "In this light . . ."
    c. "This is . . ."
    d. "Reproductive failures . . ."

10. One transitional phrase used in paragraph 4 is
    a. "The tendency."
    b. "This is."
    c. "The problem is."
    d. "As a result."

CHAPTER 7
FOLLOWING THOUGHT PATTERNS

Directions: *Read each of the following textbook excerpts and answer the questions that follow.*

A. The heart is a large muscular organ capable of powerful contractions that propel blood into vessels. The human heart consists of four chambers, called the right and left atria and right and left ventricles. Blood flows through each chamber in a specific sequence. Chambers are separated by valves, which open and close automatically, to ensure that blood flows only in one direction.

—Mix, Farber, and King, *Biology*, 2e, p. 663

1. The organizational pattern used in this excerpt is
   a. time sequence.
   b. problem-solution.
   c. definition.
   d. comparison-contrast.

2. The directional words that help identify the pattern used in this excerpt are
   a. "powerful contractions."
   b. "consists of."
   c. "in a specific sequence."
   d. "in one direction."

B. All objects continually radiate energy. Why, then, doesn't the temperature of all objects continually decrease? The answer is that all objects also continually absorb radiant energy. If an object is radiating more energy than it is absorbing, its temperature does decrease; but if an object is absorbing more energy than it is emitting, its temperature increases. An object that is warmer than its surroundings emits more energy than it receives, and therefore it cools; an object colder than its surroundings is a net gainer of energy, and its temperature therefore increases. An object whose temperature is constant, then, emits as much radiant energy as it receives. If it receives none, it will radiate away all its available energy, and its temperature will approach absolute zero.

—Hewitt, *Conceptual Physics*, 7e, p. 272

3. The organizational pattern used in this excerpt is
   a. cause-and-effect.
   b. time sequence.
   c. enumeration.
   d. definition.

4. The directional word that helps identify the pattern used in this excerpt is
   a. "therefore."
   b. "energy."
   c. "temperature."
   d. "but."

C. Small businesses are likely to have less formal purchasing processes. A small retail grocer might, for example, purchase a computer system after visiting a few suppliers to compare prices and features, while a large grocery chain might collect bids from a specified number of vendors and then evaluate those bids on pre-established criteria. Usually, fewer individuals are involved in the decision-making process for a small business. The owner of the small business, for example, may make all decisions, and a larger business may operate with a buying committee of several people.

—Kinnear, Bernhardt, and Krentler, *Principles of Marketing*, 4e, p. 218

5. The organizational pattern used in this excerpt is
   a. definition.
   b. comparison-contrast.
   c. time sequence.
   d. enumeration.

6. The primary type of supporting evidence used in this excerpt is
   a. descriptions.
   b. statistics.
   c. examples.
   d. citation of research evidence.

D. The pretext for full-scale intervention in Vietnam came in late July 1964. On July 30, South Vietnamese PT (patrol torpedo) boats attacked bases in the Gulf of Tonkin inside North Vietnamese waters. Simultaneously, the *Maddox,* an American destroyer, steamed into the area to disrupt North Vietnamese communication facilities. On August 2, possibly seeing the two separate missions as a combined maneuver against them, the North Vietnamese sent out several

PT boats to attack the destroyer. The *Maddox* fired, sinking one of the attackers, then radioed the news to Washington. Johnson ordered another ship into the bay. On August 3, both destroyers reported another attack, although somewhat later. The president ordered American planes to retaliate by bombing inside North Vietnam.

—adapted from Wilson, et al., *The Pursuit of Liberty, volume two*, 3e, pp. 492-93

7. The organizational pattern used in this excerpt is
   a. comparison-contrast.
   b. definition.
   c. enumeration.
   d. time sequence.

8. The primary type of supporting evidence used in this excerpt is
   a. examples.
   b. facts.
   c. descriptions.
   d. citation of research evidence.

E. Certain techniques can aid in the generation of creative alternates. Brainstorming, commonly used in group discussions, encourages participants to come up with as many new ideas as possible, no matter how outrageous. Other group members are not permitted to criticize or ridicule. Another approach to generating alternatives, developed by the U.S. Navy, is called "Blast! Then Refine." Group members tackle a recurring problem afresh, erasing from their minds all solutions and procedures tried in the past. The group then re-evaluates its original objectives, modifies them if necessary, and devises new solutions to the problem. Other techniques—including trial and error—are also useful in this stage of decision making.

—Pride, Hughes and Kapoor, *Business*, 53, p. 189

9. The organizational pattern used in this excerpt is
   a. enumeration.
   b. cause-effect.
   c. time sequence.
   d. comparison-contrast.

10. The directional word that helps identify the pattern used in this excerpt is
    a. "Certain."
    b. "Another."
    c. "group."
    d. "useful."

CHAPTER 8
READING GRAPHICS AND TECHNICAL WRITING

Part I. Interpreting a Table

Directions: *Answer questions 1-4 based on the following table.*

Minority Populations in 1990 and Projected for 2000 and 2050

	1990		2000		2050	
	Number (thousands)	Percentage of Population	Number (thousands)	Percentage of Population	Number (thousands)	Percentage of Population
African American	29,986	12.1	33,834	12.3	57,316	15.0
Latino	22,354	9.0	30,602	11.1	80,675	21.1
Asian American	7,273	2.9	11,582	4.2	38,765	10.1
American Indian	1,959	0.8	2,096	0.7	4,078	1.0

Source: U.S. Bureau of the Census (1993)

1. The subject of this table is
   a. minority populations.
   b. the 1990 census.
   c. the percentage of immigrants in the United States.
   d. the U.S. Bureau of the Census.

2. In 1990, the total number of African Americans was
   a. 29,986.
   b. 33,834.
   c. 29,986,000.
   d. 33,834,000.

3. Between 1990 and 2050, the group that will experience the largest percentage increase in population is
   a. African Americans.
   b. Latinos.
   c. Asian Americans.
   d. American Indians.

Part II. Interpreting Pie Charts

Directions: *Answer questions 4-6 based on the following pie charts.*

4. The purpose of this pair of pie charts is to
   a. show gender discrimination in the work force.
   b. compare the occupations of men and women in the U.S.
   c. recruit men and women for farming, forestry, and fishing occupations.
   d. indicate which professions are better suited to men.

5. The occupation employing the largest percentage of women is
   a. managerial, professional, specialty.
   b. service.
   c. technical, sales, administrative support.
   d. operators, fabricators, laborers.

6. The occupation employing the smallest percentage of men is
   a. operators, fabricators, laborers.
   b. precision production, craft, repair.
   c. service.
   d. farming, forestry, fishing.

Occupations of Women and Men in the U.S.

WOMEN

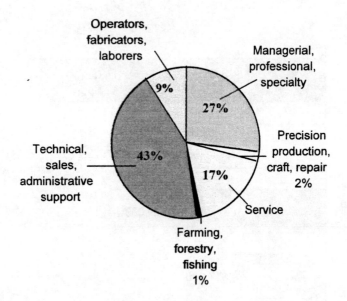

MEN

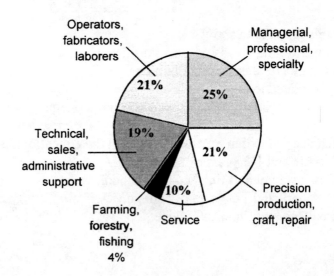

Source: U.S. Bureau of the Census (1990).

111

Part III. Interpreting a Bar Graph

Directions: *Answer questions 7-10 based on the following bar graph.*

Education and Income

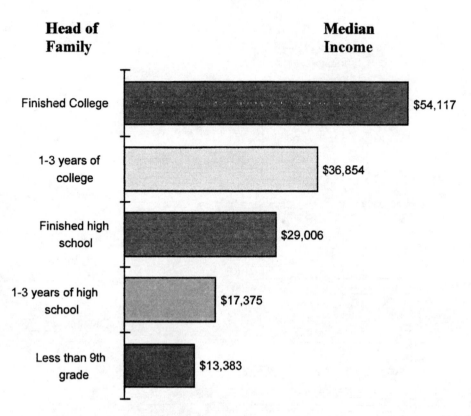

Source: U.S. Bureau of the Census (1994).

7. The purpose of this graph is to show
   a. how much education the heads of most families have.
   b. what the median income is for most families.
   c. how income is related to education level.
   d. the number of high school graduates who go on to college.

8. The largest difference in median income is between the educational levels of
   a. less than 9th grade and 1-3 years of high school.
   b. 1-3 years of high school and finished high school.
   c. finished high school and 1-3 years of college.
   d. 1-3 years of college and finished college.

9. The smallest difference in median income is between the educational levels of
   a. less than 9th grade and 1-3 years of high school.
   b. 1-3 years of high school and finished high school.
   c. finished high school and 1-3 years of college.
   d. 1-3 years of college and finished college.

10. The trend shown by this graph is that the
   a. higher the level of education, the lower the income.
   b. lower the level of education, the higher the income.
   c. higher the level of education, the higher the income.
   d. level of education has no effect on the level of income.

CHAPTER 9
READING AND EVALUATING ELECTRONIC SOURCES

Part I. Reading Electronic Sources

Directions: *Answer questions 1-6 based on the situation described below.*

Ana is a freshman at a large university. She is required to use the Internet for research in many of her classes, and her instructors routinely communicate with students using e-mail. Ana has decided to create a Web site for Hispanic students, so she has been looking at the Web sites of other student groups to get ideas. From the home page of the Korean student Web site, for example, she was able to visit the Web sites of several other student groups, a feature she wants to incorporate on the site she is designing.

1. To gain access to the Internet, Ana needs a computer and all of the following *except*
   a. a modem.
   b. a CD-ROM.
   c. an Internet service provider.
   d. a browser.

2. For a research paper in health class, Ana wants to browse the Web for sites on holistic and alternative medicines. The best type of tool for a broad search of these topics would be a
   a. search engine.
   b. meta-search engine.
   c. subject directory.
   d. uniform resource locator (URL).

3. Ana's research paper will include both traditional print and hypertext sources. One difference she may find between the two types of text is that
   a. print text tends to be more multi-directional.
   b. hypertext typically consists of longer, more detailed sentences and paragraphs.
   c. she should be able to read the computer screen much faster than on the printed page.
   d. hypertext will require her to make more decisions about the direction of her research.

4. While she is online visiting other student group Web sites, Ana would use bookmarking to
   a. find a book on the subject of designing Web sites.
   b. record Web site addresses so she can access them easily later.
   c. mark her place in a section of hypertext.
   d. retrace the path she followed while visiting other sites.

5. As compared to a letter, an e-mail from Ana's instructors probably is less
   a. formal.
   b. conversational.
   c. expedient.
   d. concise.

6. Ana was able to visit other Web sites from the Korean students' home page by using features called
   a. navigational buttons.
   b. relative links.
   c. remote links.
   d. nodes.

Part II. Evaluating Internet Sources

Directions: *Next to each of the following statements, write T if the statement is true or F if the statement is false.*

7. _____ Informational Web sites typically include .edu or .gov as part of their address.

8. _____ All Web sites ending in .org are sponsored by nonprofit groups.

9. _____ Information about the timeliness of a Web site is usually provided on the homepage.

10. _____ Web sites are required to include the author's full name and credentials.

CHAPTER 10
CRITICAL THINKING AND READING

Directions: *Read the following passage and then answer questions 1-10.*

I start my day here at five o'clock. I get up and prepare all the children's clothes. If there's shoes to shine, I do it in the morning. About seven o'clock I bathe the children. I leave the baby with the baby sitter and I go to work at the settlement house. I work until twelve o'clock. Sometimes I'll work longer if I have to go to welfare and get a check for somebody. When I get back, I try to make hot food for the kids to eat. In the afternoon it's pretty well on my own. I scrub and clean and cook and do whatever I have to do.

Welfare makes you feel like you're nothing. Like you're laying back and not doing anything and it's falling in your lap. But you must understand, mothers, too, work. My house is clean. I've been scrubbing since this morning. You could check my clothes, all washed and ironed. I'm home and I'm working. I am a working mother.

A job that a woman in a house is doing is a tedious job—especially if you want to do it right. If you do it slipshod, then it's not so bad. I'm pretty much of a perfectionist. I tell my kids, hang a towel. I don't want it thrown away. That is very hard. It's a constant game of picking up this, picking up that. And putting this away, so the house'll be clean.

Some men work eight hours a day. There are mothers that work eleven, twelve hours a day. We get up at night, a baby vomits, you have to be calling the doctor, you have to be changing the baby. When you do get a break, really? You don't. This is an all-around job, day and night. Why do they say it's charity? We're working for our money. I am working for this check. It is not charity. We are giving some kind of home to these children.

I'm so busy all day I don't have time to daydream. I pray a lot. I pray to God to give me strength. If He should take a child away from me, to have the strength to accept it. It's His kid. He just borrowed him to me.

I used to get in and close the door. Now I speak up for my right. I walk with my head up. If I want to wear big earrings, I do. If I'm overweight, that's too bad. I've gotten completely over feeling where I'm little. I'm working now, I'm pulling my weight. I'm gonna get off welfare in time, that's my goal—get off.

It's living off welfare and feeling that you're taking something for nothing the way people have said. You get to think maybe you are. You get to think, Why am I so stupid? Why can't I work? Why do I have to live this way? It's not enough to live on anyway. You feel degraded.

The other day I was at the hospital and I went to pay my bill. This nurse came and gave me the green card. Green card is for welfare. She went right in front of me and gave it to the cashier. She said, "I wish I could stay home and let the money fall in my lap." I felt rotten. I was just burning inside. You hear this all the way around you. The doctor doesn't even look at you. People are ashamed to show that green card. Why can't a woman just get a check in the mail: Here, this check is for you. Forget welfare. You're a mother who works.

This nurse, to her way of thinking, she represents the working people. The ones with the green card, we represent the lazy no-goods. This is what she was saying. They're the good ones and we're the bad guys.

—Terkel, *Working*, pp. 303-4

1. The author of this passage is a
   a. professional writer.
   b. welfare mother.
   c. social worker.
   d. taxpayer against welfare.

2. The tone of the author primarily conveys her
   a. gratitude for public assistance.
   b. satisfaction with her situation.
   c. desire to be understood.
   d. hope for the future.

3. The author's purpose in writing this passage was to
   a. lobby for reform of welfare laws.
   b. expose people who misuse welfare.
   c. express bitterness toward those who represent the working world.
   d. explain how unfairly society treats welfare recipients.

4. The statement that best represents the author's primary argument is
   a. All women work harder than men.
   b. All welfare recipients work.
   c. People make welfare recipients feel bad about themselves.
   d. People don't receive much money on welfare.

5. The author supports her argument with
   a. facts.
   b. personal experience.
   c. statistics.
   d. analogies.

6. The statement which best supports the author's primary argument is
   a. "Welfare makes you feel like you're nothing."
   b. "I'm pretty much of a perfectionist."
   c. "My house is clean."
   d. "Now I speak up for my right."

7. The author states, "A job that a woman in a house is doing is a tedious job—especially if you want to do it right." This statement can best be described as
   a. a fact.
   b. an opinion.
   c. an informed opinion.
   d. an inference.

8. All of the following words help the reader to make inferences *except*
   a. scrub.
   b. nurse.
   c. rotten.
   d. degraded.

9. Of the following statements made by the author, the one that is an opinion is
   a. "I work until twelve o'clock."
   b. "I pray a lot."
   c. "This nurse came and gave me the green card."
   d. "They're the good ones, and we're the bad guys."

10. The author reveals her bias by
    a. taking one side of an argument and not recognizing opposing views.
    b. taking a radical stand on a controversial issue.
    c. supporting an unpopular argument.
    d. arguing both sides of the issue.

CHAPTER 11
EXPANDING YOUR VOCABULARY

Part I. Dictionary Skills

Directions: *Use a dictionary to answer questions 1-5.*

1. The correct phonetic spelling for the word <u>parsimony</u> is
   a. par see mow nee.
   b. par sa mow nee.
   c. par see mow na.
   d. pair sa mow na.

2. The adjective form for the word <u>gerund</u> is
   a. gerundival.
   b. gerundivial.
   c. gerundively.
   d. gerundial.

3. The definition of the word <u>draffish</u> is
   a. worthless.
   b. muddy or soiled.
   c. having a trim appearance.
   d. coarse or rough.

4. In parts of speech, the word <u>liefer</u> is
   a. a pronoun.
   b. a noun.
   c. a verb.
   d. an adverb.

5. The origin of the word <u>internecine</u> is
   a. English.
   b. French.
   c. Latin.
   d. Greek.

Part II. Using a Thesaurus

Directions: *Use a thesaurus to answer questions 6-10.*

6. A synonym for the word <u>gangling</u> is
   a. hoodlum.
   b. dangling.
   c. prisoner.
   d. awkward.

7. In parts of speech, the word <u>melange</u> is
   a. a noun.
   b. a verb.
   c. an adverb.
   d. an adjective.

8. The word <u>argentum</u> is a synonym for
   a. dollar.
   b. silver.
   c. gold.
   d. coin.

9. Another word for <u>taciturn</u> is
   a. articulate.
   b. circular.
   c. sign.
   d. reserved.

10. Another word for <u>prolix</u> is
    a. productive.
    b. preface.
    c. verbose.
    d. professional.

CHAPTER 12
USING CONTEXT AND WORD PARTS

Part I. Context Clues

Directions: *For questions 1-5, use your knowledge of context clues to choose a synonym or brief definition for the underlined word in each sentence.*

1. When solving a complex math problem, it is better to be <u>punctilious</u> and get it right than to be careless and risk getting it wrong.
    a. timely
    b. careful
    c. mistaken
    d. risky

2. Although most people would have been hurt or angry by such severe criticism, he remained <u>undaunted</u> by it.
    a. unaffected
    b. bothered
    c. disappointed
    d. puzzled

3. All of the people in church looked prayerful bowing their heads, except for the small child who appeared <u>impious</u> with his continuous chatter.
    a. cheerful
    b. religious
    c. disrespectful
    d. unhappy

4. Extroverted people tend to be outgoing and talkative, while introverted people are more <u>reticent</u>.
    a. reserved
    b. showy
    c. overbearing
    d. helpless

5. The meal was prepared perfectly, but the young woman found it <u>repugnant</u>.
    a. overpriced
    b. lovely
    c. unappealing
    d. delicious

Part II. Word Parts

Directions: *For questions 6-10, use your knowledge of word parts to determine the meaning of the underlined word in each sentence.*

6. If an agreement were described as <u>bilateral,</u> you would expect it to involve
   a. one party only.
   b. two parties.
   c. three parties.
   d. many parties.

7. In the word <u>telepathy,</u> the root refers to
   a. disease.
   b. feeling.
   c. distance.
   d. sound.

8. The prefix <u>circum</u> means
   a. with.
   b. against.
   c. around.
   d. away.

9. The root that means <u>study</u> is
   a. bio.
   b. mort.
   c. logy.
   d. graph.

10. The root that means <u>tell</u> or <u>say</u> is
    a. aud.
    b. cred.
    c. vis.
    d. dict.

CHAPTER 13
TEXTBOOK HIGHLIGHTING AND MARKING

Directions: *Read the following passage and then answer questions 1-10.*

SLEEPING AND DREAMING

Sleep alters our consciousness by reducing alertness and the perception of events occurring around us. Sleep is a normal process, yet it is one we do not understand well. We are seldom aware or conscious of our own sleeping, even though we may spend more than 200,000 hours of our lifetime asleep. Just as the level or degree of our awareness varies during the day, so does our sleep vary in its level or quality throughout the night and from night to night.

1

Our best indicators of sleep are measurements of brain activity and muscle tone. The electroencephalograph (EEG) is an instrument that records electrical activity in the brain. It does so through small electrodes that are pasted onto the scalp. The process is slightly messy, but it is not painful. An electromyograph (EMG) produces a record of a muscle's activity or relaxation.

2

When you are in a calm, relaxed state, with your eyes closed but not yet asleep, your EEG pattern shows a rhythmic cycle of brain waves called alpha activity. In this presleep stage, we find relatively smooth EEG waves cycling 8 to 12 times per second. If, as you sit or lie there, you start worrying about events of the day, or try to solve a problem, smooth alpha waves become disrupted and are replaced by an apparently random pattern of heightened electrical activity typical of what we find in wakefulness.

3

As you drift from relaxation into sleep, brain waves change, as alpha waves give way to the stages of sleep. The EEG tracings of sleeping subjects can be divided into four different stages.

4

Stage 1 is a very light sleep from which you can be easily aroused. The smooth, cyclical alpha pattern disappears, replaced by the slower *theta waves* (3-7 cycles per second). The amplitude, or magnitude, of the electrical activity also lessens considerably. At the same time, your breathing is becoming more regular, and your

5

heart rate is slowing and blood pressure is decreasing. This stage does not last very long—generally less than 10 minutes. Then you start to slide into Stage 2 sleep.

In **Stage 2**, the EEG pattern is similar to Stage 1—low amplitude with no noticeable wavelike pattern. The difference is that we now see *sleep spindles* in the EEG record. These are brief, high-amplitude bursts of electrical activity that occur with regularity (about every 15 seconds or so). You're really getting off to sleep now, but still can be easily awakened.

6

In **Stage 3**, you're going into a deep sleep. There is a reduction in the brain's electrical activity. We can clearly make out *delta wave* activity in your EEG. Delta waves are high, slow waves (from 0.5 to 3 cycles every second). In Stage 3, delta waves constitute between 20 and 50 percent of your EEG pattern. Your internal functions (temperature, heart rate, breathing) are lowering and slowing. It is difficult to wake you now.

7

In **Stage 4**, you are in a deep sleep. Your EEG record is virtually filled with slow delta waves, recurring over and over again (as opposed to Stage 2, where delta waves comprise only a portion of your brain wave activity). Readings from an electromyogram indicate that your muscles have become totally relaxed. About 15 percent of your night's sleep will be spent in this stage of deep sleep.

8

It usually takes about an hour to go from Stage 1 to Stage 4, depending on such things as how tired you are and the physical conditions surrounding you. After an hour's passage through these four stages, the sequence reverses itself. You go back through Stage 3, then to Stage 2, but before going through the cycle again, something remarkable happens. Your eyes start to move rapidly under closed eyelids.

9

—Gerow, *Essentials of Psychology*, 2e, pp. 181-83

1. The best words to highlight in the first sentence of paragraph 1 are
   a. sleep occurring around us.
   b. consciousness reducing alertness.
   c. perception of events.
   d. sleep reducing alertness perception.

2. In the third sentence of paragraph 1, the best words to highlight are
   a. spend 200,000 hours asleep.
   b. seldom aware of our own sleeping.
   c. we may spend hours asleep.
   d. 200,000 hours of our lifetime.

3. In the fourth sentence of paragraph 1, the best words to highlight are
   a. just as the level.
   b. awareness varies during day.
   c. sleep vary throughout night.
   d. from night to night.

4. In paragraph 2, the words that would *not* be important enough to highlight are
   a. best indicators measurements brain muscle.
   b. EEG records electrical activity.
   c. process slightly messy.
   d. EMG record muscle's activity.

5. In paragraph 3, the words that should be highlighted are
   a. eyes closed not asleep.
   b. alpha activity presleep stage smooth waves.
   c. if you start worrying about the events of the day.
   d. try to solve a problem.

6. The most helpful marginal notation for paragraphs 5-8 would be
   a. writing alpha –> theta –> sleep spindles –> delta.
   b. circling EEG every time it appears.
   c. numbering each of the stages with Roman numerals.
   d. placing asterisks next to the last sentence of each paragraph.

7. In paragraph 6, the most important words to highlight are
   a. EEG pattern.
   b. sleep spindles.
   c. off to sleep.
   d. but still can be.

8. In paragraph 7, the words that should *not* be highlighted are
   a. we can clearly make.
   b. deep sleep.
   c. delta wave.
   d. between 20 and 50 percent.

9. The best summary phrase for paragraph 8 would be
   a. EEG record filled.
   b. deep delta sleep.
   c. unlike Stage 2.
   d. muscles are relaxed.

10. In paragraph 9, the most important words to highlight are
    a. it usually takes.
    b. physical conditions surrounding you.
    c. you go back.
    d. eyes start to move rapidly.

CHAPTER 14
METHODS OF ORGANIZING INFORMATION

Directions: *Read the passage about music below and complete the tasks that follow.*

Music is a form of expressive culture whose medium consists of sounds, patterned in different rhythmic combinations. The elements of music are tones, percussion, and rhythm. A tone is a sound that has a certain duration, quality, and (most important) a certain highness or lowness, determined by the frequency of its sound vibrations (a tone's highness or lowness is called its pitch). Percussion consists of toneless sounds made by striking something. Music is made up of patterned combinations of tones (usually assembled into melodies), toneless percussive sounds, and rhythms. These patterned combinations differ among societies, and studying them within a given cultural context or cross-culturally is called ethnomusicology.

1

The sounds out of which human beings make music can be produced in two different ways. First, the human body can be used as a sound-producing instrument. The human voice can produce an enormous range of different tones, and percussive sounds can be made by clapping the hands, stamping the feet, or slapping the thighs. All of these sounds are elements of music encountered cross-culturally. Second, music can be produced by instruments, which range in complexity and musical potential from simple rattles made from dried gourds to technologically complex electric organs and sound synthesizers.

2

Defined as a form of expressive culture consisting of patterned sounds, music is found in every society. Moreover, even though music (like language) was until recently an ephemeral art—meaning that worlds of musical art disappeared as soon as they were performed—music (like oral art) probably played an important part in prehistoric cultures, too. The evidence lies not only in the fact that every culture known today creates music; there are also archaeological hints distributed worldwide: ancient instruments such as whistles, flutes, drums, rattles, and bullroarers (elongated pieces of bone or other materials, which when attached to cords and whirled about the head produce an eerie, prolonged tone).

3

—Hicks and Gwynne, *Cultural Anthropology*, 2e, p. 35

Part I. Outlining

Directions: *Complete the outline below by answering questions 1-7 on the following page.*

I. Musical Terms

    A. Definition of music

    B. [Second major idea]

        1. Tone

            a. Duration

            b. Quality

            c. [Third minor detail]

        2. [Second important detail]

        3. Rhythm

    C. Ethnomusicology

II. [Second major topic]

    A. [First major idea]

        1. [First important detail]

        2. Percussive sounds

    B. Using Instruments

        1. Simple

        2. Complex

III. [Third major topic]

    A. Important part of prehistoric cultures

        1. All of today's cultures have it

        2. Archaeological hints/ancient instruments

1. The best choice to go in place of [Second major idea] is
   a. Expressive culture.
   b. Elements of music.
   c. Medium that consists of sounds.
   d. Different rhythmic combinations.

2. The best choice to go in place of [Third minor detail] is
   a. Highness.
   b. Lowness.
   c. Pitch.
   d. Frequency.

3. The best choice to go in place of [Second important detail] is
   a. Toneless sounds.
   b. Patterned combinations.
   c. Percussion.
   d. Melodies.

4. The best choice to go in place of [Second major topic] is
   a. Ways of producing music.
   b. The human body.
   c. Cultural context.
   d. Sound-producing instrument.

5. The best choice to go in place of [First major idea] is
   a. Sound-producing instrument.
   b. Enormous range of tones.
   c. Musical potential.
   d. Using the human body.

6. The best choice to go in place of [First important detail] is
   a. Voice.
   b. Clapping hands.
   c. Stamping feet.
   d. Slapping thighs.

7. The best choice to go in place of [Third major topic] is
   a. Expressive culture.
   b. Patterned sounds.
   c. Found in every society.
   d. An ephemeral art.

Part II. Summarizing

Directions: *Use the passage about music to answer questions 8-10.*

8. The best sentence to use in a summary of paragraph 1 would be
   a. Music is made up of tones, percussion, and rhythm.
   b. A medium consists of sounds.
   c. Most important is a certain highness or lowness.
   d. Music is usually assembled into melodies.

9. The best sentence to use in a summary of paragraph 2 would be
   a. Sounds can be made by clapping hands or stamping feet.
   b. We can produce music by using our bodies or by using instruments.
   c. Slapping the thighs is a percussive sound.
   d. Simple rattles can be made from dried gourds.

10. The best sentence to use in a summary of paragraph 3 would be
    a. Worlds of musical art disappeared as soon as they were performed.
    b. Some ancient instruments are whistles, flutes, drums, and rattles.
    c. Music is found in every society.
    d. Bullroarers produce an eerie, prolonged tone.

CHAPTER 15
STUDY AND REVIEW STRATEGIES

Directions: *Read the passage below and complete the tasks that follow.*

INTIMACY VERSUS INDEPENDENCE

Women speak and hear a language of connection and intimacy whereas men speak and hear a language of status and independence. John Gray, writing in *Men Are From Mars, Women Are From Venus*, claims that women are more interested in people and feelings, and men are more interested in objects and things. The "things" Gray refers to include whatever can help men express power by creating results, achieving goals, and doing things by themselves. This is how men prove their competence and strengthen their egos. 1

These characteristics, as it turns out, answer several related questions, for example, "Why don't men ever stop and ask for directions when they are lost?" Men take great pride in handling problems on their own. "Why involve others," they might think, "when I can do it myself?" Asking others for help when they can do it themselves is perceived as a sign of weakness. Also, there is a great deal of pride to be gained from having resolved the problem of how to get there. (They seldom admit to being lost.) That is why, when in dialogue the men involved attempt to solve the problems their partners are facing. Women, on the other hand, enjoying intimacy or connection, spend a lot of time supporting, helping, and nurturing; thus, they see no problem in seeking others—especially when lost—who can offer these features. Sharing and relating is natural, easy, and proper. 2

Other related questions can be answered with the "intimacy versus independence" base. Women often wonder why men become absorbed in sports; men often wonder why women become absorbed in soap operas or romance novels. It should be clear with respect to interests in sports and soap operas, however, that they do not split evenly along gender-based lines. Many females enjoy sports; many males enjoy soap operas. But this does not explain the predominant gender-based interests. Think about it. Men value power, competency, efficiency, and achievement. These characteristics are clearly demonstrated 3 on the athletic field. Women value love, communication, beauty, and relationships. These characteristics are clearly demonstrated in soap operas and romance novels.

This is but one area where rules of communication collide. Women use talk to build and sustain connections with others. Men use talk to convey information and establish their independent status. These differences, obviously, give rise to many others. With just these two ideas as starting points, however, the number of misunderstandings that are likely to follow is not surprising.

4

—Weaver, *Understanding Interpersonal Communication*, 7e, p. 253

Part I. Paraphrasing

Directions: *Use the passage to answer questions 1-6 about paraphrasing.*

1. In paragraph 1, the best paraphrase for the first sentence is
    a. Women speak and hear a language of connection and intimacy.
    b. Women focus on intimacy and men focus on power and independence.
    c. Men speak and hear a language of status and independence.
    d. Women understand intimacy whereas men understand status.

2. In paragraph 1, the best paraphrase for the last two sentences is
    a. To prove themselves, men create results, achieve goals, and do things by themselves.
    b. The "things" Gray refers to include whatever can help men express power.
    c. Men create results by doing things by themselves.
    d. Men prove their competence and strengthen their egos.

3. In paragraph 2, the best paraphrase for the first sentence is
    a. Why don't men ask for directions when they are lost?
    b. There are several related questions.
    c. Men's characteristics answer questions such as why they don't ask for directions when they are lost.
    d. Men should ask for directions when they are lost.

4. In paragraph 2, the best paraphrase for the last sentence is
    a. Sharing and relating is natural, easy, and proper.
    b. For women, it's natural to share and relate.
    c. Men can't share and relate.
    d. Sharing is natural and relating is proper.

5. In paragraph 3, the best paraphrase for the last four sentences is
   a. Men value power, competency, efficiency, and achievement.
   b. Men value characteristics shown in athletics and women value characteristics shown in romantic fiction.
   c. Women value love, communication, beauty, and relationships.
   d. Some characteristics are on the athletic field and some are in soap operas and romance novels.

6. The best paraphrase for paragraph 4 is
   a. This is one area where rules of communication collide.
   b. Men establish their independent status.
   c. Misunderstandings are likely to follow.
   d. Men and women communicate for such different purposes that misunderstandings are inevitable.

Part II. Self-Testing

Directions: *Use the passage to answer questions 7-10.*

7. The most effective self-test question based on this passage would be
   a. a multiple-choice question on gender-based interests.
   b. a true/false question on how men handle problems.
   c. an open-ended question on how men and women communicate for different purposes.
   d. a set of matching questions that asks what different characteristics men and women value.

8. An example of a question at the application level of thinking is
   a. What are the chief characteristics of men's language?
   b. Why are women comfortable asking others for help?
   c. Give an example that shows how the language focus of women and men differs.
   d. Does the description of the language of women and men agree with your experience?

9. The level of thinking demonstrated by the question "What gender is more interested in connection and intimacy?" is
   a. knowledge.
   b. application.
   c. synthesis.
   d. analysis.

10. The level of thinking demonstrated by the question "How effectively does this passage describe gender-based differences in communication?" is
    a. knowledge.
    b. comprehension.
    c. synthesis.
    d. evaluation.

CHAPTER 16
PREPARING FOR EXAMS

Part I. Study Sheets

Directions: *Read the passage below and complete the tasks that follow.*

COURSE OF A COMMUNICABLE DISEASE

Many (though not all) diseases pass through the following sequence of events. This sequence is especially characteristic of **acute diseases**, those with a sudden onset and a short duration. **Chronic** communicable diseases, those with a gradual onset and a long duration, tend not to follow such a distinctive course.   1

After a pathogen has entered the body, there is a period of time before any symptoms appear; this is the **incubation period.** During this time, the pathogen is multiplying, adapting to its new host, and sometimes migrating to a specific part of the body. Incubation   2
periods can be as short as a few hours (for food poisoning) or as long as many years (for AIDS and Hansen's disease [leprosy]). They are typically a few days to a few weeks.

The **prodromal period** is the phase during which nonspecific symptoms appear following the incubation period. The first symptoms to appear tend to be similar for many diseases—fever, headache, aching body, and a vague feeling of discomfort or malaise. It is   3
usually impossible to diagnose a disease by its prodromal symptoms. Most people in this stage of disease will continue with their normal routine of work or school activities, which is unfortunate, because *the late incubation period and prodromal period are the most contagious times for many diseases.*

After a few hours to several days of prodromal symptoms, the more specific symptoms of a disease appear. Now, diagnosis on the basis of symptoms is possible in the case of   4
some diseases, though many illnesses are best diagnosed using laboratory tests. During the **typical illness period**, the pathogen and the body defenses are engaging in a life-or-death

battle. Usually the body defenses, possibly aided by antimicrobial drugs, are victorious and recovery begins.

Convalescence is the period of recovery after a disease. As a person is regaining health, even though most disease symptoms may have abated, *some of the pathogens remain alive in the body,* and are held in check by the body's defenses. Improper diet or lack or rest may weaken the body defenses, allowing the pathogen to break free and multiply once again. This causes disease symptoms to return, and is known as a **relapse.** Following any illness, it is advisable to resume normal activities gradually, allowing the body defenses to eradicate the pathogen completely.

5

The convalescence period is followed by one of three possible states: immunity, resusceptibility, or the carrier state. **Immunity** is protection from a repeated attack of a disease, lasting anywhere from a few months to a lifetime. This type of immunity is highly specific and often does not even extend to closely related forms of the same illness. For example, having influenza confers immunity only to the specific strain of virus that was involved. Recovery without immunity means that a person may become infected again by any new contact with the pathogen. This is the case for diseases such as gonorrhea, for which no immunity usually develops. Someone who has recovered from a disease, but still harbors a pathogen, is called an **active carrier.** This active carrier state occurs with many diseases, such as hepatitis B, mononucleosis, and typhoid fever. For many pathogens, including those causing gonorrhea and genital *Chlamydia,* a person may pass directly from infection to the carrier state without experiencing any symptoms.

6

—Byer and Shainberg, *Living Well,* 2e, pp. 558-60

Part I. Study Sheet

Directions: *Complete the study sheet below by answering questions 1-6 on the following page.*

<u>Communicable Diseases</u>

TYPE	ONSET	[A]
[B]	Sudden	Short
Chronic	Gradual	Long

<u>Stages of Disease</u>

PERIOD	WHEN	WHAT HAPPENS	OTHER FACTS
Incubation	[C]	Pathogen adapts, multiplies, may migrate	Can last a few hours to many years
[D]	After incubation	Nonspecific symptoms: fever, headache, aching body, vague discomfort	Most contagious period
Typical illness	After prodromal	[E]	Diagnosis now possible
Convalescence/ Recovery	After disease	Most symptoms are gone but some pathogens remain	[F]

1. The best word to go in place of [A] is
   a. Incubation.
   b. Sequence.
   c. Duration.
   d. Events.

2. The best word to go in place of [B] is
   a. Disease.
   b. Acute.
   c. Sequence.
   d. Communicable.

3. The best phrase to go in place of [C] is
   a. Before symptoms appear.
   b. A period of time.
   c. During this time.
   d. A pathogen enters the body.

4. The best word to go in place of [D] is
   a. Phase.
   b. Nonspecific.
   c. Malaise.
   d. Prodromal.

5. The best phrase to go in place of [E] is
   a. Specific symptoms; body defends itself.
   b. A few hours to several days.
   c. In the case of some diseases.
   d. Antimicrobial drugs.

6. The best phrase to go in place of [F] is
   a. Weaken the body defenses.
   b. Poor diet or insufficient rest can cause relapse.
   c. Following any illness.
   d. Eradicate the pathogen completely.

Part II. Index Card System

Directions: *Use the last paragraph of the passage to answer questions 7-9.*

7. The best phrase for the front of an index card with "Immunity, resusceptibility, or carrier" on the back is
   a. Termination of illness.
   b. Convalescence period.
   c. Recovery without immunity.
   d. Protection from disease.

8. The best phrase for the back of an index card with "Immunity" on the front is
   a. A repeated attack of a disease.
   b. Having influenza.
   c. Temporary or permanent protection from a repeated attack of a disease.
   d. Protection for a lifetime.

9. The best phrase for the back of an index card with "Active carrier" on the front is
   a. A pathogen for which no immunity develops.
   b. A disease such as hepatitis B, mononucleosis, or typhoid fever.
   c. A person who becomes reinfected by new contact with the disease.
   d. A person who has recovered from a disease but still harbors a pathogen.

Part III. Predicting Essay Questions

Directions: *Use the passage to answer question 10.*

10. The best example of an essay question at the knowledge level of thinking would be
    a. What are the implications of the prodromal period for communicable diseases such as AIDS?
    b. Describe the typical course of an acute communicable disease.
    c. Describe your own experience with illness, recovery, and, if applicable, relapse.
    d. Evaluate the accuracy, reliability, and timeliness of this passage.

CHAPTER 17
TAKING EXAMS

Part I. Planning Your Time

Directions: *Assume that you have three hours to complete your final exam in history. Use the following information to estimate the amount of time you should spend on each part of the exam, then answer questions 1-5.*

TYPE OF QUESTION	NUMBER OF QUESTIONS	TOTAL POINTS
Multiple-choice	30	30
True/false	20	10
Matching	10	10
Essay	3	50

1. The total amount of time you should spend prereading the exam is
    a. 1 minute.
    b. 3-5 minutes.
    c. 15-20 minutes.
    d. at least 30 minutes.

2. The amount of time you should spend on the multiple-choice questions is
    a. 10-15 minutes.
    b. 30-40 minutes.
    c. 60-80 minutes
    d. at least 80 minutes.

3. The amount of time you should spend on the true/false questions is
    a. 10-15 minutes.
    b. 30-40 minutes.
    c. 60-80 minutes.
    d. at least 80 minutes.

4. The amount of time you should spend on the matching questions is
   a. 10-15 minutes.
   b. 30-40 minutes.
   c. 60-80 minutes.
   d. at least 80 minutes.

5. The amount of time you should spend on the essay questions is
   a. 10-15 minutes.
   b. 30-40 minutes.
   c. 60-80 minutes.
   d. at least 100 minutes.

Part II. Analyzing Essay Questions

Directions: *Each of the questions below contains an essay question from an exam. Use your knowledge of the parts of an essay question (topic, key words, and limiting words) to answer questions 6-10.*

6. "Describe the use of symbolism in *Moby Dick*." In this essay question, the key word or phrase is
   a. "Describe."
   b. "use of."
   c. "symbolism."
   d. "*Moby Dick*."

7. "Trace the reproductive cycles of angiosperms and gymnosperms." In this essay question, the topic is
   a. reproductive cycles.
   b. angiosperms.
   c. gymnosperms.
   d. angiosperms and gymnosperms.

8. "Identify and compare the three stages of African literature." In this essay question, the limiting word or phrase is
   a. "Identify."
   b. "compare."
   c. "three stages."
   d. "African literature."

9. "Discuss the reasons why, although tropical plants have very large leaves and most desert plants have very small leaves, cactus grows equally well in both habitats." In this essay question, the topic is
   a. tropical plants.
   b. desert plants.
   c. cactus.
   d. habitats.

10. In the essay question in number 9, the key word or phrase is
   a. "Discuss."
   b. "reasons why."
   c. "although."
   d. "equally well."

CHAPTER 18
IMPROVING YOUR READING RATE AND FLEXIBILITY

Directions: *Give yourself two to three minutes to skim the following article, then cover it with a sheet of paper and answer questions 1-10.*

THE REAL WORLD
Bilingual Children

What happens to children who are exposed to two or more languages from the beginning? How confusing is this for a child? And how can parents ease the process? As least two important practical questions surround this issue of bilingualism:

- Should parents who speak different native languages try to expose their children to both, or will that only confuse their children to both, or will that only confuse the child and make any kind of language learning harder? What's the best way to do this?

- If a child arrives at school age without speaking the dominant language of schooling, what is the best way for the child to acquire that second language?

Learning Two Languages at the Same Time

Parents should have no fears about exposing their child to two or more languages from the very beginning. Such simultaneous exposure does seem to result in slightly slower early steps in word learning and sentence construction, and the child will initially "mix" words or grammar from the two languages in individual sentences. But bilingual children catch up rapidly to their monolingual peers.

The experts agree that the best way to help a child to learn two languages fluently is to speak both languages to the child from the beginning, *especially* if the two languages come at the child from different sources. For example, if Mom's native language is English and Dad's is Italian, Mom should speak only English to the infant/toddler and Dad should speak only Italian. If both parents speak both languages to the child or mix them up in their own speech, this is a much more difficult situation for the child and language learning will be delayed. It will also work if one language is always spoken at home and the other is spoken in a day-care center, with playmates, or in some other outside situation.

Bilingual Education

For many children, the need to be bilingual does not begin in the home, but only at school age. In the United States today, there are 2.5 million school-age children for whom English is not the primary language of the home. Many of those children arrive at school with little or no facility in English. Educators have had to grapple with the task of teaching children a second language at the same time that they are trying to teach them subject matter such as reading and mathematics. The problem for the schools has been to figure out the best way to do this. Should the child learn basic academic skills in his native language and only later learn English as a second language? Or will some combination of the two work?

The research findings are messy. Still, one thread does run through it all: Neither full immersion nor English-as-a-second-language programs are as effective as truly bilingual programs in which the child is given at least some of her basic instruction in subject matter in her native language in the first year or two of school but is also exposed to the second language in the same classroom. After several years of such combined instruction, the child makes a rapid transition to full use of the second language for all instruction. Interestingly, in her analysis of this research, Ann Willig has found that the ideal arrangement is very much like what works best at home with toddlers: If some subjects are always taught in one language and other subjects in the other language, children learn the second language most easily. But if each sentence is translated, children do not learn the new language as quickly or as well.

—Conger and Galambos, *Adolescence and Youth*, 53, p. 230

1. The title of the article is
   a. "The Languages of Parents and Children."
   b. "Bilingual Children in Public Schools."
   c. "The Real World (Bilingual Children)."
   d. "Learning to Speak English."

2. The issue that the article focuses mostly on is
   a. the best way to teach two languages to children.
   b. the conflicts encountered by bilingual children.
   c. research findings on the academic performance of bilingual children.
   d. whether parents should teach their children a foreign language.

3. The author's view on whether parents should expose young children to two languages is that
   a. it is better to teach a child only one language at a time.
   b. children can be expected to learn a second language only after they've mastered the first.
   c. teachers should be required to teach a second language to a child if that language is spoken in the home.
   d. parents should not be afraid to expose their children to two or more languages.

4. In the author's view, the *best* way to help a child learn two languages fluently is to speak
   a. both languages to the child from the beginning.
   b. a second language to the child only after the child is fluent in the first.
   c. both languages to a child but wait until the child is at least school age.
   d. only one language to the child to avoid confusion.

5. According to the article, the need to be bilingual begins for many children
   a. at school age.
   b. at home.
   c. during the preschool years.
   d. as soon as the child develops language.

6. According to the article, research findings on this topic are
   a. consistent.
   b. abundant.
   c. messy.
   d. rare.

7. Research indicates that the best way to teach bilingual children is through
   a. full immersion programs.
   b. English-as-a-second-language (ESL) programs.
   c. truly bilingual programs or combined instruction.
   d. the same methods as monolingual children.

8. With appropriate instruction, a bilingual child can master the second language in
   a. six months.
   b. nine months.
   c. one year.
   d. several years.

9. When each sentence is translated for a bilingual child, the child typically
   a. learns the second language more slowly.
   b. learns the second language better.
   c. never learns the second language.
   d. quickly forgets the first language.

10. The author's purpose in writing this article is to
    a. criticize.
    b. entertain.
    c. persuade.
    d. inform.

ANSWER KEY TO MASTERY TESTS

CHAPTER 1

1. a
2. d
3. c
4. d
5. a

6. c
7. d
8. c
9. c
10. b

CHAPTER 2

1. a
2. c
3. c
4. b
5. d

6. b
7. a
8. c
9. d
10. c

11. c
12. a
13. d
14. a
15. c

CHAPTER 3

1. c
2. a
3. c
4. d
5. c

6. b
7. d
8. d
9. b
10. c

CHAPTER 4

1. c
2. c
3. b
4. b
5. d

6. b
7. b
8. c
9. a
10. b

CHAPTER 5

1. d
2. c
3. b
4. a
5. a

6. a
7. a
8. d
9. d
10. b

CHAPTER 6

1.	a	6.	a
2.	d	7.	a
3.	b	8.	c
4.	d	9.	a
5.	c	10.	d

CHAPTER 7

1.	c	6.	c
2.	b	7.	d
3.	a	8.	b
4.	a	9.	a
5.	b	10.	b

CHAPTER 8

1.	a	6.	d
2.	d	7.	c
3.	b	8.	d
4.	b	9.	a
5.	c	10.	c

CHAPTER 9

1.	b	6.	c
2.	c	7.	T
3.	d	8.	F
4.	b	9.	T
5.	a	10.	F

CHAPTER 10

1.	b	6.	a
2.	c	7.	c
3.	d	8.	b
4.	c	9.	d
5.	b	10.	a

CHAPTER 11

1.	b	6.	d
2.	d	7.	a
3.	a	8.	b
4.	d	9.	d
5.	c	10.	c

CHAPTER 12

1.	b	6.	b
2.	a	7.	b
3.	c	8.	c
4.	a	9.	c
5.	c	10.	d

CHAPTER 13

1.	d	6.	a
2.	b	7.	b
3.	c	8.	b
4.	c	9.	b
5.	b	10.	d

CHAPTER 14

1.	b	6.	a
2.	c	7.	c
3.	c	8.	a
4.	a	9.	b
5.	d	10.	c

CHAPTER 15

1.	b	6.	d
2.	a	7.	c
3.	c	8.	c
4.	b	9.	a
5.	b	10.	d

CHAPTER 16

1.	c	6.	b
2.	b	7.	a
3.	a	8.	c
4.	d	9.	d
5.	a	10.	b

CHAPTER 17

1.	b	6.	a
2.	b	7.	d
3.	a	8.	c
4.	a	9.	c
5.	d	10.	a

CHAPTER 18

1.	c	6.	c
2.	a	7.	c
3.	d	8.	d
4.	a	9.	a
5.	a	10.	d

PART FOUR

ADDITIONAL PRACTICE EXERCISES

SET I   *USING CONTEXT AND WORD PARTS*

Exercise 1

Directions: *Each of the following statements contains an underlined word. Use either your knowledge of word parts (prefixes, roots, and suffixes) or the context of the sentence to select the choice that best completes each sentence.*

_____ 1.   If something were described as <u>bilinear</u>, you would expect it to have
      a.   one line.
      b.   two lines.
      c.   many lines.
      d.   no lines.

_____ 2.   The word <u>introspective</u> contains
      a.   a root only.
      b.   a prefix and a root only.
      c.   a root and a suffix only.
      d.   a prefix, a root, and a suffix.

_____ 3.   All of the following prefixes indicate a negative *except*
      a.   contra.
      b.   un.
      c.   trans.
      d.   anti.

_____ 4.   If a man were described to you as <u>pseudointellectual</u>, you would expect him to be
      a.   extremely smart.
      b.   not as smart as he pretends to be.
      c.   overly smart.
      d.   not smart at all.

_____ 5.   The opposite meaning of the prefix <u>sub-</u> is indicated by the prefix
      a.   super-.
      b.   retro-.
      c.   inter-.
      d.   mid-.

_____ 6.   The root <u>photo</u> means
      a.   write.
      b.   change.
      c.   see.
      d.   light.

_____ 7. The root that means <u>life</u> is
   a. aster.
   b. bio.
   c. theo.
   d. chrono.

_____ 8. The roots <u>graph</u> and <u>script</u> both have to do with
   a. hearing.
   b. taking.
   c. writing.
   d. turning.

_____ 9. If a woman were accused of <u>polyandry,</u> she would have
   a. no husband.
   b. one husband.
   c. a deceased husband.
   d. more than one husband.

_____ 10. All of the following suffixes mean <u>one who</u> except
   a. -ee.
   b. —eer.
   c. —ist.
   d. -y.

Exercise 2

Directions: *Each of the following statements contains an underlined word. Determine the word's meaning by using either your knowledge of word parts (prefixes, roots, and suffixes) or the context of the sentence. Select the choice that most clearly states the correct meaning of the word.*

_____ 1. He <u>couched</u> a threat in his words.
a. hinted at
b. shouted
c. declared
d. wrote

_____ 2. In ancient Egypt, the sun was <u>venerated</u> as a god.
a. depicted
b. drawn
c. worshipped
d. denounced

_____ 3. Hugh felt strongly in favor of private schools, but his wife was more <u>ambivalent</u>.
a. uncertain
b. opposed
c. supportive
d. content

_____ 4. Andy was a real <u>devotee</u> of the arts.
a. participant
b. critic
c. fan
d. detractor

_____ 5. Melanoma, a form of skin cancer caused by overexposure to the sun, is <u>endemic</u> among fair-skinned populations.
a. unlikely
b. prevalent
c. impossible
d. rare

_____ 6. Lisa's negative comments only served to <u>exacerbate</u> the situation.
a. relieve
b. distract
c. make light of
d. worsen

_____ 7. After the town meeting, a <u>fracas</u> broke out among supporters of the opposing candidates.
   a. debate
   b. cheer
   c. brawl
   d. contest

_____ 8. In addition to her physical ailments, the patient was diagnosed with <u>autophobia</u>.
   a. fear of others
   b. fear of oneself
   c. fear of pain
   d. fear of disease

_____ 9. As soon as we moved the ficus tree to the other room, it began to <u>defoliate</u>.
   a. lose its leaves
   b. grow more leaves
   c. thrive
   d. dry up

_____ 10. Enoch was a lawyer before he turned to <u>theology.</u>
   a. writing
   b. teaching
   c. study of religion
   d. study of life.

Exercise 3

Directions: *Each of the following statements contains an underlined word. Determine the word's meaning by using either your knowledge of word parts (prefixes, roots, and suffixes) or the context of the sentence. Select the choice that most clearly states the correct meaning of the word.*

_____ 1. The cottage was in a <u>bucolic</u> setting, with excellent views of the countryside from every window.
   a. sophisticated
   b. rural
   c. boring
   d. urban

_____ 2. A Spanish fort was built at the <u>confluence</u> of two rivers.
   a. end
   b. beginning
   c. banks
   d. joining

_____ 3. Finally, after being sedated, the violent patient became <u>noncombative</u>.
   a. untalkative
   b. unresponsive
   c. uncooperative
   d. unresistant

_____ 4. Candace wore a red, low-cut dress to the party, but her sister was dressed more <u>decorously</u>.
   a. fashionably
   b. warmly
   c. fancy
   d. modestly

_____ 5. Most species of sponges are <u>marine</u>; only about 150 species are freshwater sponges.
   a. green
   b. from the sea
   c. plant-like
   d. organic

_____ 6. Her last five tax returns were audited after the IRS discovered an <u>egregious</u> error on her latest return.
   a. notably bad
   b. minor
   c. simple
   d. clerical

_____ 7. The hound wore a <u>lugubrious</u> expression—perhaps hoping to gain the sympathy of the family and a scrap from the table—but everyone just laughed at him.
a. guilty
b. comically sad
c. cheerful
d. ashamed

_____ 8. Even thought the situation was his own fault, the naval officer blamed his <u>subordinate</u>.
a. commanding officer
b. peer
c. person of lower rank
d. civilian

_____ 9. The finishing school's advertisement read, "Youth and beauty are <u>ephemeral</u>—good manners last forever."
a. temporary
b. permanent
c. unimportant
d. admirable

_____ 10. Having grown up in south Florida, she thought of Minnesota as <u>hyperborean</u>.
a. less populated
b. less friendly
c. uneducated
d. extremely cold

Exercise 4

Directions: *Each of the following statements contains an underlined word. Determine the word's meaning by using either your knowledge of word parts (prefixes, roots, and suffixes) or the context of the sentence. Select the choice that most clearly states the correct meaning of the word.*

_____ 1. The professor used so many <u>polysyllabic</u> words that her students had difficulty understanding her.
   a. one syllable
   b. obscure
   c. technical
   d. many syllables

_____ 2. After doing well in the polls, the candidate gave an <u>ebullient</u> speech to his supporters.
   a. apologetic
   b. humble
   c. enthusiastic
   d. sober

_____ 3. Lin looked with <u>chagrin</u> at the stain where her coffee had spilled.
   a. pleasure
   b. surprise
   c. indifference
   d. embarrassment

_____ 4. Unlike other male-dominated species, Indian elephants live in a <u>matriarchal</u> society.
   a. aggressive
   b. nonthreatening
   c. led by females
   d. passive

_____ 5. One member of the Everest expedition was killed when he stumbled and fell into a <u>crevasse</u>.
   a. cliff
   b. ditch
   c. ice storm
   d. deep crack

6. The old man avoided his family; in fact, he <u>eschewed</u> the company of any man or woman who knew his past.
    a. sought out
    b. enjoyed
    c. shunned
    d. welcomed

7. After 30 years of <u>desuetude</u>, the old truck had to be hauled out of the weeds and towed to the junkyard.
    a. excellent care
    b. wrecked
    c. overuse
    d. abandonment

8. The book was a <u>compilation</u> of essays by Depression-era writers.
    a. criticism
    b. collection
    c. excerpt
    d. analysis

9. The <u>intertidal</u> zone is home to many organisms, including sea stars and anemones.
    a. between tides
    b. underwater
    c. river bank
    d. island

10. The weekend retreat was intended to be a time for <u>introspection</u>.
    a. socializing
    b. group discussions
    c. looking within
    d. counseling

Exercise 5

Directions: *Each of the following statements contains an underlined word. Determine the word's meaning by using either your knowledge of word parts (prefixes, roots, and suffixes) or the context of the sentence. Select the choice that most clearly states the correct meaning of the word.*

_____ 1. They built two houses on the mountainside, with the guest cabin <u>subjacent</u> to the main lodge.
   a. far away from
   b. at a higher elevation
   c. at a lower elevation
   d. adjoining

_____ 2. The television program featured a <u>retrospective</u> on the late cartoonist's career.
   a. review
   b. preview
   c. musical piece
   d. comedy

_____ 3. The children were exhausted after their <u>transatlantic</u> flight.
   a. cross-country
   b. along the Atlantic coast
   c. across the Atlantic Ocean
   d. away from the Atlantic Ocean

_____ 4. Humans are <u>bipeds</u>.
   a. both plant and meat eaters
   b. two-footed
   c. either left or right handed
   d. dependent on wheels

_____ 5. The international school prided itself on its <u>multilingual</u> curriculum.
   a. equal opportunity
   b. small student-teacher ratio
   c. two languages
   d. many languages

_____ 6. Six stars in the Pleiades–an <u>asterism</u> in the constellation Taurus–are visible to the naked eye.
   a. cluster of stars
   b. planetary system
   c. satellite
   d. meteor shower

_____ 7. The company celebrated its <u>semicentennial</u> in 2002.
    a. 25th anniversary
    b. 50th anniversary
    c. 100th anniversary
    d. 200th anniversary

_____ 8. We finally had to give away our parrot because it <u>vociferated</u> day and night!
    a. slept constantly
    b. called out loudly
    c. dropped feathers
    d. flew around

_____ 9. Langston Hughes was a <u>prolific</u> writer of poems, plays, short stories, song lyrics, and children's books.
    a. minor
    b. conservative
    c. unknown
    d. productive

_____ 10. The second-grader recited the preamble to the Constitution with such <u>aplomb</u> that she received a standing ovation from the audience.
    a. composure
    b. gratitude
    c. nervousness
    d. mistakes

SET II   *VOCABULARY IN CONTEXT (PASSAGES)*

Directions: *Each of the following passages contains several underlined words. Using either your knowledge of word parts or the context of the sentence, and a dictionary, if necessary, determine the meaning of each underlined word.*

Exercise 1

The Web consists of hypertext <u>interspersed</u> with multimedia elements such as graphical images, sound clips, and video clips. Hypertext is a dynamic variation on traditional text that allows you to <u>digress</u> and view a related document by just clicking on a mouse. No <u>hierarchy</u> exists to make one document more important than any other, and paths through related documents often uncover rich collections of related information. Hypertext enables associations across multiple authors that sometimes resemble <u>collective</u> authorship but without the overhead of a coordinated effort. A pointer from a main text to a related document is called a link or a hyperlink. Most documents on the Web contain links to additional Web pages. You can <u>traverse</u> a link by clicking it with your mouse.

—Lehnert, *Light on the Internet*, pp. 12-13

_____   1.   The word <u>interspersed</u> means
          a.   interrupted.
          b.   placed among.
          c.   removed.
          d.   separated.

_____   2.   The word <u>digress</u> means
          a.   wander or go off the path.
          b.   quit.
          c.   discuss.
          d.   reverse.

_____   3.   The word <u>hierarchy</u> means
          a.   distinction.
          b.   rule.
          c.   ordered arrangement.
          d.   randomness.

_____ 4. The word <u>collective</u> means
   a. group.
   b. copyrighted.
   c. singular.
   d. professional.

_____ 5. The word <u>traverse</u> means
   a. imitate.
   b. eliminate.
   c. ignore or bypass.
   d. travel over or go across.

Exercise 2

As a general, Washington was not a brilliant strategist like Napoleon. Neither was he a <u>tactician</u> of the quality of Caesar or Robert E. Lee. But he was a remarkable organizer and administrator—patient, thoughtful, <u>conciliatory</u>. In a way, his lack of genius made his achievements all the more impressive. He held his forces together in <u>adversity</u>, avoiding both useless slaughter and catastrophic defeat. People of all sections, from every walk of life, looked on Washington as the <u>embodiment</u> of American virtues: a man of deeds rather than words; a man of substance accustomed to luxury yet capable of enduring great hardships <u>stoically</u> and as much at home in the wilderness as an Indian; a bold Patriot, quick to take arms against British tyranny, yet <u>eminently</u> respectable. The Revolution might have been won without Washington, but it is unlikely that the free United States would have become so easily a true nation had he not been at its call.

—Garraty and Carnes, *The American Nation*, 10e, p. 133

_____ 1. The word <u>tactician</u> means
   a. scholar.
   b. expert in military tactics or maneuvers.
   c. expert in foreign policy.
   d. historical figure.

_____ 2. The word <u>conciliatory</u> means
   a. competitive.
   b. aggressive.
   c. secretive.
   d. reassuring.

_____ 3. The word <u>adversity</u> means
   a. victory.
   b. unfavorable circumstances.
   c. peacetime.
   d. desertion.

_____ 4. The word <u>embodiment</u> means
   a. emigrant.
   b. weak example.
   c. personification.
   d. opposite.

_____ 5. The word <u>stoically</u> means
   a. selfishly.
   b. emotionally.
   c. uncomplainingly.
   d. angrily.

_____ 6. The word <u>eminently</u> means
   a. not completely.
   b. outstandingly.
   c. later.
   d. originally.

Exercise 3

When the Gilded Age began, American literature was dominated by the romantic mood. Longfellow stood at the height of his fame, and the <u>lachrymose</u> Susan Warner–"tears on almost every page"–continued to turn out stories in the style of her popular _The Wide, Wide World_. Romanticism, however, had lost its creative force; most writing in the decade after 1865 was sentimental trash pandering to the <u>preconceptions</u> of middle-class readers. Most writers of fiction tended to ignore the eternal conflicts <u>inherent</u> in human nature and the social problems of the age; polite entertainment and <u>pious</u> moralizing appeared to be their only objective.

—Garraty and Carnes, _The American Nation_, 10e, p. 565

_____ 1. The word <u>lachrymose</u> means
   a. tearful.
   b. famous.
   c. forceful.
   d. brief.

_____ 2. The word <u>preconceptions</u> means
      a. controversial opinions.
      b. ideas formed in advance.
      c. previous purchases.
      d. goodwill.

_____ 3. The word <u>inherent</u> means
      a. inborn.
      b. unnecessary.
      c. uncharacteristic.
      d. obvious.

_____ 4. The word <u>pious</u> means
      a. private.
      b. religious.
      c. polite.
      d. angry.

Exercise 4

Protists [a type of organism] are a diverse group of mostly <u>unicellular</u> eukaryotes. Almost any aquatic environment is home to great numbers of protists. Most species require oxygen, but some are <u>anaerobic</u>, living in the mud at the bottom of lakes and stagnant ponds or thriving in the digestive tracts of animals. Protists occupy a <u>pivotal</u> position in the history of life: The first ones arose from prokaryotes, and their descendants gave rise to all plants, fungi, and animals, as well as to all modern protists. The cells of many protists are among the most <u>elaborate</u> in the world. This level of cellular complexity is not really surprising, for each unicellular protist is a complete eukaryotic organism <u>analogous</u> to an entire animal or plant.

—Campbell, Mitchell, and Reece, *Biology*, 3e, p. 335

_____ 1. The word <u>unicellular</u> means
      a. no cells.
      b. single-celled.
      c. double-celled.
      d. many cells.

_____ 2. The word <u>anaerobic</u> means
      a. without oxygen.
      b. in water.
      c. using motion.
      d. simple.

3. The word pivotal means
   a. opposite.
   b. questionable.
   c. critical or vitally important.
   d. controversial.

4. The word elaborate means
   a. complex.
   b. basic.
   c. simple.
   d. unimportant.

5. The word analogous means
   a. unable to reproduce.
   b. unique.
   c. complicated.
   d. similar or comparable.

Exercise 5

Ancient legends allude to the special qualities of spiders and their webs--qualities that arise from unique properties of molecules. Web builders spin their webs with remarkable speed and agility. A particular web can take only an hour to construct, yet its symmetry and efficacy in capturing insects are without parallel. Silk proteins make a spiderweb remarkably strong and resilient, able to withstand a struggling insect's attempts to escape. In an orb web, the strands extending straight out from the center of the orb are composed of dry, relatively inelastic proteins; they maintain the web's position and overall shape. In contrast, the orb's spiraling strand, which actually captures insects, is wet, sticky, and highly elastic.

—Campbell, Mitchell, and Reece, *Biology*, 3e, pp. 32-33

1. The word allude means
   a. avoid
   b. refer.
   c. omit.
   d. determine.

2. The word agility means
   a. nimbleness.
   b. speed.
   c. productivity.
   d. pleasure.

171

_____ 3. The word <u>efficacy</u> means
   a. destruction.
   b. wastefulness.
   c. effectiveness.
   d. balance.

_____ 4. The word <u>resilient</u> means
   a. rigid.
   b. elastic.
   c. wide.
   d. fragile.

_____ 5. The word <u>inelastic</u> means
   a. highly adaptable.
   b. wet.
   c. unnatural.
   d. not flexible.

SET III   *MAIN IDEA/DETAILS (PASSAGES)*

Directions: *Read each of the following passages. Then, using your knowledge of the parts of a paragraph (topics, main ideas, topic sentences, details, and transitions), answer the questions that follow each passage.*

Exercise 1

Sitting at the pinnacle of the American judicial system is the U.S. Supreme Court. The court does much more for the American political system than decide individual cases. Among its most important functions are resolving conflicts among the states and maintaining national supremacy in the law. The Supreme Court also plays an important role in ensuring uniformity in the interpretation of national laws. For example, in 1984 Congress created a federal sentencing commission to write guidelines aimed at reducing the wide disparities in punishment for similar crimes tried in federal courts. By 1989, more than 150 federal district judges had declared the law unconstitutional, and another 115 had ruled it valid. Only the Supreme Court could resolve this inconsistency in the administration of justice, which it did when it upheld the law.

There are nine justices on the Supreme Court: eight associates and one chief justice (only members of the Supreme Court are called justices; all others are called judges). The Constitution does not require this number, however, and there have been as few as six justices and as many as ten. The size of the Supreme Court was altered many times between 1801 and 1869. In 1866, Congress reduced the size of the Court from ten to eight members so that President Andrew Johnson could not nominate new justices to fill two vacancies. When Ulysses S. Grant took office, Congress increased the number of justices to nine, because it had confidence that he would nominate members to its liking. Since then, the number of justices has remained stable.

—Edwards, Wattenberg, Lineberry, *Government in America*, 9e, p. 535

_____   1.   The topic of the first paragraph is the
                 a. appeal process.
                 b. functions of the Supreme Court.
                 c. interpretation of laws.
                 d. structure of the federal court system.

_____ 2. In the first paragraph, the topic sentence begins with the words
   a. "Sitting at the pinnacle . . ."
   b. "The Court does much more . . ."
   c. "By 1989 . . ."
   d. "Only the Supreme Court . . ."

_____ 3. One transitional phrase used in the first paragraph is
   a. "much more."
   b. "among the states."
   c. "for example."
   d. "which it did."

_____ 4. The topic of the second paragraph is
   a. inconsistencies in the administration of justice.
   b. Constitutional requirements.
   c. the number of Supreme Court justices.
   d. President Andrew Johnson.

_____ 5. The main idea of the second paragraph is that
   a. only members of the Supreme Court are called justices.
   b. President Andrew Johnson was prevented from nominating two justices.
   c. Congress was confident that Ulysses Grant would nominate acceptable justices.
   d. The number of Supreme Court justices has fluctuated.

_____ 6. In 1866, Congress reduced the size of the Supreme Court because
   a. the Constitution required Congress to do so.
   b. Congress wanted to prevent President Johnson from filling two vacancies.
   c. no judges were qualified to become new Supreme Court justices.
   d. the current justices could not reach a consensus.

Exercise 2

In an individualist culture you're responsible for yourself and perhaps your immediate family; in a collectivist culture you're responsible for the entire group. Success, in an individualist culture, is measured by the extent to which you surpass other members of your group; you would take pride in standing out from the crowd. And your heroes—in the media, for example—are likely to be those who are unique and who stand apart. In a collectivist culture success is measured by your contribution to the achievements of the group as a whole; you would take pride in your similarity to other members of your group. Your heroes, in contrast, are more likely to be team players who don't stand out from the rest of the group's members. In an individualist culture you're responsible to your own conscience and responsibility is largely an individual matter. In a collectivist culture you're responsible to the rules of the social group and responsibility for an accomplishment or a failure is shared by all members. Competition is promoted in individualist cultures while cooperation is promoted in collectivist cultures.

Those who come from cultures that are highly individual and competitive may find public criticism a normal part of the learning process. Those who come from cultures that are more collective and that emphasize the group rather than the individual are likely to find giving and receiving public criticism uncomfortable. Thus, people from individual cultures may readily criticize others and are likely to expect the same "courtesy" from other listeners. After all, this person might reason, if I'm going to criticize your skills to help you improve, I expect you to help me in the same way. Persons from collective cultures, on the other hand, may feel that it's more important to be polite and courteous than to help someone learn a skill. In some cultures, being kind to the person is more important than telling the truth, and so members may say things that are complimentary but untrue in a logical sense.

—DeVito, *The Elements of Public Speaking*, 7e, p. 82

_____ 1. The topic of the first paragraph is
   a. differences between cultures.
   b. individualist cultures.
   c. collectivist cultures.
   d. competition.

_____ 2. In the first paragraph, the topic sentence begins with the words
   a. "In an individualist . . ."
   b. "Success, in an . . ."
   c. "Your heroes . . ."
   d. "Competition is . . ."

_____ 3. One transitional phrase used in the first paragraph is
   a. "you're responsible."
   b. "as a whole."
   c. "in contrast."
   d. "is shared."

_____ 4. The main idea of the second paragraph is that
    a. public criticism is a normal part of the learning process.
    b. people from different cultures approach public criticism differently.
    c. criticism is acceptable as long as it is constructive and helpful.
    d. being kind to a person is more important than telling the truth.

_____ 5. In an individualistic culture, a hero is most likely to be
    a. someone who conforms to the culture.
    b. a team player within the group.
    c. a highly cooperative individual.
    d. a unique person with outstanding accomplishments.

Exercise 3

Narratives are stories, and they are often useful as supporting materials in a speech. Narratives give the audience what it wants: a good story. Listeners seem to perk up automatically when a story is told. If the narrative is a personal one, it will likely increase your credibility and show you as a real person. Listeners like to know about speakers, and the personal narrative meets this desire. Notice how you remember the little stories noted personalities tell in television interviews.

The main value of narration is that it allows you to bring an abstract concept down to specifics. For example, to illustrate friendship and love, you might recount the mythical story of Damon and Pythias. After being sentenced to death for speaking out against the government by the tyrant Dionysius, Pythias asked to be allowed to return home to put his affairs in order. His friend, Damon, volunteered to remain in his place. If Pythias did not return, Damon would be executed. At the appointed time, Pythias did not return. Without animosity toward his friend, Damon prepared for his own execution. But, before the sentence could be carried out, Pythias returned, apologized for his unavoidable delay, and asked that his friend be set free. So impressed was Dionysius by this friendship that he pardoned Pythias and asked if he could join the two of them in this extraordinary friendship. This brief story illustrates friendship and love in a way that a definition could never do.

—DeVito, *The Elements of Public Speaking*, 7e, p. 164

_____ 1. The topic of the first paragraph is
    a. narratives.
    b. supporting materials.
    c. credibility.
    d. television interviews.

_____ 2. In the first paragraph, the topic sentence begins with the words
    a. "Narratives give . . ."
    b. "Narratives are . . ."
    c. "Listeners seem . . ."
    d. "Listeners like . . ."

_____ 3. The topic of the second paragraph is
    a. abstract concepts.
    b. friendship and love.
    c. the main value of narration.
    d. the mythical story of Dionysius and Pythias.

_____ 4. One transitional phrase in the second paragraph is
    a. "the main value."
    b. "for example."
    c. "at the appointed time."
    d. "without animosity."

_____ 5. When used in speeches, narratives are intended to accomplish all of the following _except_
    a. capture the audience's attention.
    b. increase the speaker's credibility.
    c. make a specific concept more abstract.
    d. show the speaker as a real person.

Exercise 4

The most common form of Internet abuse is spam. Spam is unsolicited impersonal e-mail from a party who is unknown to you or with whom you have no consenting relationship. Anyone who sends out an announcement to millions of e-mail addresses is a spammer. Most e-mail spam is commercial in nature. But spam can also contain political calls for action, religious sermons, philosophical manifestos, or the incoherent ravings of someone with a mental problem.

If you're more worried about avoiding spam than generating it, you'll need to learn more about the various ways that spammers obtain e-mail addresses. Whenever you are asked to provide personal information over the Web or via e-mail, you should know what, if any, privacy policies will be applied to protect your privacy online. No laws in the United States protect the privacy rights of consumers, so users must be savvy about what goes on behind the scenes. If a company offers you a "free" e-mail account, how much information do you have to give up in order to participate? Data resellers generate a lot of revenue by selling Internet user profiles to advertisers, marketing organizations, and scam artists. Whenever anyone on the Internet offers you a free service in exchange for information, understand that you are probably being bought and sold. If the service is worth it to you, fine. But most people don't realize that they are really trading personal privacy for a free e-mail account or free space on a Web page server.

—Lehnert, *Light on the Internet*, pp. 53, 55

_____ 1. The topic of the first paragraph is
    a. e-mail.
    b. Internet abuse (spam).
    c. political calls for action.
    d. privacy issues.

_____ 2. In the first paragraph, the topic sentence begins with the words
    a. "The most common . . ."
    b. "Anyone who . . ."
    c. "Most e-mail . . ."
    d. "But spam . . ."

_____ 3. The topic of the second paragraph is
    a. how to generate spam.
    b. the privacy rights of consumers.
    c. free e-mail accounts.
    d. how spammers obtain e-mail addresses.

_____ 4. The main idea of the second paragraph is that
    a. you can avoid spam by learning how spammers obtain e-mail addresses.
    b. you should never provide personal information over the Internet.
    c. laws should be enacted to protect the privacy rights of consumers.
    d. when you accept a free e-mail account, you give up personal privacy.

_____ 5. One way that spammers obtain e-mail addresses is by
   a. buying them from data resellers.
   b. violating laws that protect the privacy rights of consumers.
   c. responding to requests for information.
   d. providing free online services.

Exercise 5

For those who want to use the Web as a serious information resource, the openly democratic nature of the Web undermines the credibility of everything on it. When anyone can publish a work and distribute it as freely as anyone else, there are no editors on hand to squelch information that is unreliable, questionable, or downright misleading. It may be intoxicating to have fast and easy access to millions of documents on thousands of topics, but what good is any of it if you can't distinguish fact from fiction? To make the Web an effective research tool for students, business people, and professionals, new skills are needed that go beyond the point-and-click mastery of a particular Web browser. Responsible information consumers need to assess the reliability of their online sources.

Some people have thrown up their hands and declared the Web useless because it offers so much questionable material and, in some cases, outright garbage. They claim that if you're truly serious about researching a topic, the local library is still your best bet. If the Web offered nothing more than the contents of newspapers and special interest magazines and books, all mixed up with less credible materials, you might indeed wonder if ease of access justifies all the extra work required to assess reliability.

In fact, there is more to the Web than the online versions of traditional printed materials. Thousands of experts post fascinating pages based on years of experience and hard-won expertise. A lot of these people are wholly legitimate and can be trusted. Moreover, many would never publish a book or even write a short article for a magazine, but they are writing their own Web pages. It would be a shame to reject their expertise just because you need to exercise caution. You also can find lecture notes for college courses and lovingly assembled resource pages on everything from the health problems of dachshunds to sheet music emporia for musicians. Science fiction fans can find spirited discussions of their favorite authors, and mothers can look for advice on solving all kinds of parenting problems (including whether to let children surf the Web).

—Lehnert, *Light on the Internet*, pp. 60-62

_____ 1. The topic of the first paragraph is
    a. information resources.
    b. credibility of Web sources.
    c. online editors.
    d. Web browsers.

_____ 2. In the first paragraph, the topic sentence begins with the words
    a. "For those . . ."
    b. "When anyone . . ."
    c. "It may be . . ."
    d. "Responsible information . . ."

_____ 3. A key supporting detail in the first paragraph is the phrase
    a. "point-and-click mastery."
    b. "distinguish fact from fiction."
    c. "it may be intoxicating."
    d. "effective research tool."

_____ 4. The main idea of the second paragraph is that
    a. the Web is useless because it offers so much questionable material.
    b. the local library is the best place to research a topic.
    c. people wonder if easy access to the Web justifies having to assess its reliability.
    d. people think the Web only offers the contents of newspapers and other print materials.

_____ 5. The topic of the third paragraph is
    a. traditional print materials.
    b. types of online information.
    c. online authors.
    d. online lecture notes.

_____ 6. In the third paragraph, the topic sentence begins with the words
    a. "In fact . . ."
    b. "Thousands of . . ."
    c. "You also . . ."
    d. "Science fiction . . ."

7. One transitional word used in the third paragraph is
   a. "traditional."
   b. "moreover."
   c. "caution."
   d. "kinds."

Exercise 6

A fruit, the ripened ovary of a flower, is a special adaptation that helps disperse seeds. Some angiosperms [flowering plants] depend on wind for dispersal. For example, the dandelion fruit acts like a kite, carrying a seed away from the parent plant on wind currents. Some other angiosperms produce fruits that hitch a free ride on animals. The cockleburs attached to the fur of a dog are fruits that may be carried miles before they open and release their seeds.

Many angiosperms produce fleshy, edible fruits that are attractive to animals as food. When a mouse eats a berry, it digests the fleshy part of the fruit, but most of the tough seeds pass unharmed through its digestive tract. The mouse may then deposit the seeds, along with a supply of natural fertilizer, some distance from where it ate the fruit. Many types of garden produce, including tomatoes, squash, and melons, as well as strawberries, apples, cherries, and oranges, are edible fruits.

The fruit of flowering plants usually develops and ripens quickly, so the seeds can be produced and dispersed in a single growing season. The dispersal of seeds in fruits is one of the main reasons angiosperms are so numerous and widespread.

—Campbell, Mitchell, and Reece, *Biology*, 3e, p. 357

1. The topic of the first paragraph is
   a. dandelions.
   b. seed dispersal.
   c. cockleburs.
   d. parent plants.

2. In the first paragraph, the topic sentence begins with the words
   a. "A fruit . . ."
   b. "Some angiosperms . . ."
   c. "For example . . ."
   d. "The cockleburs . . ."

_____ 3. One transitional phrase used in the first paragraph is
a. "a special adaptation."
b. "for dispersal."
c. "For example."
d. "like a kite."

_____ 4. The topic of the second paragraph is
a. angiosperms.
b. the dispersal of seeds through edible fruits.
c. the role of mice in seed dispersal.
d. edible fruits in gardens.

_____ 5. A key supporting detail in the second paragraph is the phrase
a. many types of garden produce are edible fruits.
b. tomatoes, squash, and melons.
c. strawberries, apples, cherries, and oranges.
d. along with a supply of natural fertilizer.

_____ 6. One of the main reasons angiosperms are so widespread is the
a. dispersal of seeds in fruits.
b. slow growing season of flowering plants.
c. fertilizers applied by gardeners.
d. fact that animals will not eat them.

Exercise 7

Animal diets vary enormously, and so do methods of feeding. Certain parasites—tapeworms, for instance—are absorptive feeders; lacking a mouth or digestive tract, they absorb nutrients through their body surface. In contrast, the majority of animals, including the great whales, are ingestive feeders; they eat (ingest) living or dead organisms, either plants or animals or both, through a mouth.

Animals that ingest both plants and animals are called omnivores. We humans are omnivores, as are crows, cockroaches, and raccoons. In contrast, plant-eaters, such as cattle, deer, gorillas, and a vast array of aquatic species that graze on algae are called herbivores. Carnivores, such as lions, sharks, hawks, spiders, and snakes, eat other animals.

Ingestive feeders use several different mechanisms to obtain their food. Suspension feeders extract food particles suspended in the surrounding water. Substrate feeders live in or on their food source and eat their way through the food. Fluid feeders obtain food by sucking nutrient-rich fluids from a living host, either a plant or an animal.

Rather than filtering food from water, eating their way through a substrate, or sucking fluids, most animals are bulk feeders, meaning they ingest relatively large pieces of food. A bulk feeder uses equipment such as tentacles, pincers, claws, poisonous fangs, or jaws and teeth to kill their prey, to tear off pieces of meat or vegetation, or to take mouthfuls of animal or plant products.

—Campbell, Mitchell, and Reece, *Biology*, 3e, p. 430

_____ 1. The topic of the first paragraph is
      a. animal diets.
      b. ingestive feeders.
      c. how animals ingest their food.
      d. absorptive feeders.

_____ 2. The main idea of the first paragraph is that
      a. methods of feeding vary among animals.
      b. tapeworms do not have a mouth or digestive tract.
      c. the majority of animals eat through a mouth.
      d. animals eat a wide variety of foods.

_____ 3. The topic of the second paragraph is
      a. omnivores.
      b. herbivores.
      c. carnivores.
      d. three animal diets.

_____ 4. The main idea of the second paragraph is that
      a. animals can be classified omnivores, herbivores, or carnivores.
      b. humans eat both plants and animals.
      c. a wide array of aquatic species graze on algae.
      d. carnivores consist of lions, sharks, hawks, spiders, and snakes.

_____ 5. The topic of the third paragraph is
      a. who ingestive feeders are.
      b. how ingestive feeders obtain food.
      c. what ingestive feeders eat.
      d. where ingestive feeders live.

_____ 6. In the third paragraph, the topic sentence begins with the words
      a. "Ingestive feeders . . ."
      b. "Suspension feeders . . ."
      c. "Substrate feeders . . ."
      d. "Fluid feeders . . ."

_____ 7. The topic of the fourth paragraph is
   a. how bulk feeders eat.
   b. the equipment of bulk feeders.
   c. what bulk feeders eat.
   d. animals that are considered bulk feeders.

_____ 8. Bulk feeders eat by
   a. filtering food particles from water.
   b. eating their way through the food source they live in or on.
   c. sucking fluids from a living host.
   d. using equipment such as tentacles or teeth to ingest relatively large pieces of food.

Exercise 8

The development of the interstate highway system, begun under Eisenhower in 1956, was a major cause of increased mobility. The new roads did far more than facilitate long-distance travel; they accelerated the shift of population to the suburbs and the consequent decline of inner-city districts.

Despite the speeds that cars maintained on them, the new highways were much safer than the old roads. The traffic death rate per mile driven fell steadily, almost entirely because of the interstates. On the other hand, the environmental impact of the system was frequently severe. Elevated roads cut ugly swaths through cities, and the cars they carried released tons of noxious exhaust fumes into urban air. Hillsides were gashed, marshes filled in, forests felled—all in the name of speed and efficiency.

—Garraty and Carnes, *The American Nation*, 10e, p. 862

_____ 1. The topic of the first paragraph is
   a. the interstate highway system.
   b. President Eisenhower.
   c. long-distance travel.
   d. population shifts.

_____ 2. The main idea of the first paragraph is that
   a. President Eisenhower began developing interstate highways in 1956.
   b. the development of the interstate highway system had several effects.
   c. new roads facilitated long-distance travel.
   d. inner-city districts declined as a result of interstate highways.

_____ 3. The main idea of the second paragraph is that
   a. the new interstate highways were much safer than the old roads.
   b. the new interstate system had positive and negative effects.
   c. elevated roads made cities more unattractive.
   d. environmental effects of the interstate system were severe.

_____ 4. One transitional phrase used in the second paragraph is
   a. "rate per mile."
   b. "On the other hand."
   c. "all in the name."
   d. "tons of noxious fumes."

Exercise 9

Some young people, known generally as hippies, were so "turned off" by the modern world that they retreated from it, finding refuge in communes, drugs, and mystical religions, often wandering aimlessly from place to place. During the 1960s and 1970s, groups of them could be found in every big city in the United States and Europe.

The hippies developed a counterculture so directly opposite to the way of life of their parents' generation as to suggest to critics that they were still dominated by the culture they rejected. They wore old blue jeans and (it seemed) any nondescript garments they happened to find at hand. Males hippies wore their hair long and grew beards. Females avoided makeup and other devices more conventional women used to make themselves more attractive to men. Both sexes rejected the old Protestant ethic; being part of the hippie world meant not caring about money or material goods or power over other people. Love was more important than money or influence, feelings more significant than thought, natural things superior to anything manufactured.

—Garraty and Carnes, _The American Nation_, 10e, pp. 878-79

_____ 1. The topic of the first paragraph is
   a. communes.
   b. drugs.
   c. mystical religions.
   d. hippies.

_____ 2. The main idea of the first paragraph is that
        a. groups of hippies could be found in every major city.
        b. hippies rejected the modern world and retreated from it.
        c. hippies lived in communes.
        d. hippies wandered aimlessly from place to place.

_____ 3. In the second paragraph, the topic sentence begins with the words
        a. "The hippies . . ."
        b. "They wore . . ."
        c. "Both sexes . . ."
        d. "Love was . . ."

_____ 4. Hippies cared most about
        a. money.
        b. material possessions.
        c. power over other people.
        d. love.

ANSWER KEY TO ADDITIONAL PRACTICE EXERCISES

SET 1

Exercise 1

1.	b	6.	d
2.	d	7.	b
3.	c	8.	c
4.	b	9.	d
5.	a	10.	d

Exercise 2

1.	a	6.	d
2.	c	7.	c
3.	a	8.	b
4.	c	9.	a
5.	b	10.	c

Exercise 3

1.	b	6.	a
2.	d	7.	b
3.	d	8.	c
4.	d	9.	a
5.	b	10.	d

Exercise 4

1.	d	6.	c
2.	c	7.	d
3.	d	8.	b
4.	c	9.	a
5.	d	10.	c

Exercise 5

1.	c	6.	a
2.	a	7.	b
3.	c	8.	b
4.	b	9.	d
5.	d	10.	a

SET II

Exercise 1

1.   b
2.   a
3.   c
4.   a
5.   d

Exercise 2

1.   b
2.   d
3.   b
4.   c
5.   c
6.   b

Exercise 3

1.   a
2.   b
3.   a
4.   b

Exercise 4

1.   b
2.   a
3.   c
4.   a
5.   d

Exercise 5

1.   b
2.   a
3.   c
4.   b
5.   d

SET III

Exercise 1

1.   b
2.   b
3.   c
4.   c
5.   d
6.   b

Exercise 2

1.   a
2.   d
3.   c
4.   b
5.   d

Exercise 3

1.   a
2.   b
3.   c
4.   b
5.   c

Exercise 4

1.   b
2.   a
3.   d
4.   a
5.   a

Exercise 5

1.   b
2.   d
3.   d
4.   c
5.   b
6.   a
7.   b

Exercise 6

1.   b
2.   a
3.   c
4.   b
5.   a
6.   a

Exercise 7

1.   c
2.   a
3.   d
4.   a
5.   b
6.   a
7.   a
8.   d

Exercise 8

1.   a
2.   b
3.   b
4.   b

Exercise 9

1.   d
2.   b
3.   a
4.   d

CREDITS

Mastery Test, Chapter 5

Donald G. Kaufman and Cecilia M. Franz, *Biosphere 2000: Protecting Our Global Environment.* Dubuque, IA: Kendall/Hunt Publishing Co., 1993, pp. 561-563.

Mastery Test, Chapter 6

Robert A. Wallace, *Biology: The World of Life,* 6th edition. New York: Addison-Wesley Educational Publishers, Inc., 1992, pp. 828-829.

Mastery Test, Chapter 7

Michael C. Mix, et al., *Biology: The Network of Life*, 2nd edition. New York: Addison-Wesley Educational Publishers, Inc., 1996, p. 663.

Paul G. Hewitt, ***Conceptual Physics***, 7th **edition. New York: Addison-Wesley Educational Publishers, Inc., 1993, p. 272.**

Thomas C. Kinnear, et al., *Principles of Marketing*, 4th edition. New York: Addison-Wesley Educational Publishers, Inc., 1995, p. 218.

R. Jackson Wilson, et al., *The Pursuit of Liberty: A History of the American People, Vol. Two*, 3rd edition. New York: Addison-Wesley Educational Publishers, Inc., 1996, pp. 492-493.

William M. Pride, et al., ***Business***, 5th **edition. Boston: Houghton Mifflin Company, 1996, p. 189.**

Mastery Test, Chapter 10

From "Jesusita Novarro" from ***Working*** **by Studs Terkel. Copyright 1972, 1974 by Studs Terkel.** Reprinted by permission of Donadio & Ashworth, Inc. Literary Agency.

Mastery Test, Chapter 13

Josh R. Gerow, *Essentials of Psychology*, 2nd edition. New York: Addison-Wesley Educational Publishers, Inc., 1996, pp. 181-183.

Mastery Test, Chapter 14

David Hicks and Margaret A. Gwynne, *Cultural Anthrophology*, 2nd edition. New York: Addison-Wesley Educational Publishers, Inc., 1996, p. 355.

Mastery Test, Chapter 15

Richard L. Weaver, *Understanding Interpersonal Communication*, 7th edition. New York: Addison-Wesley Educational Publishers, Inc., 1996, p. 253.

Curtis O. Byer and Louis W. Shainberg, *Living Well: Health in Your Hands*, 2nd edition. New York: Addison-Wesley Educational Publishers, Inc., 1995, pp. 558-560.

Mastery Test, Chapter 18

John Janeway Conger and Nancy L. Galambos, *Adolescence and Youth*, 5th edition. New York: Addison-Wesley Educational Publishers, Inc., 1997, p. 230.

Additional Practice Exercises (Set II)

Exercise 1: Wendy G. Lehnert, *Light on the Internet*. New York: Addison Wesley Longman, Inc., 1999, pp. 12-13.

Exercise 2: John A. Garraty and Mark C. Carnes, *The American Nation,* 10th edition. New York: Addison Wesley Longman, Inc., 2000, p. 133.

Exercise 3: John A. Garraty and Mark C. Carnes, *The American Nation,* 10th edition. New York: Addison Wesley Longman, Inc., 2000, p. 565.

Exercise 4: Neil A. Campbell, Lawrence G. Mitchell, and Jane B. Reece, *Biology: Concepts & Connections,* 3rd edition. New York: Addison Wesley Longman, Inc., 2000, p. 335.

Exercise 5: Neil A. Campbell, Lawrence G. Mitchell, and Jane B. Reece, *Biology: Concepts & Connections,* 3rd edition. New York: Addison Wesley Longman, Inc., 2000, pp. 32-33.

Additional Practice Exercises (Set III)

Exercise 1: George C. Edwards, III, Martin P. Wattenberg, and Robert L. Lineberry, *Government in America,* 9th edition. New York: Addison-Wesley Educational Publishers, Inc., 2000, p. 535.

Exercise 2: Joseph A. DeVito, *The Elements of Public Speaking,* 7th edition. New York: Addison Wesley Longman, Inc., 2000, p. 82.

Exercise 3: Joseph A. DeVito, *The Elements of Public Speaking,* 7th edition. New York: Addison Wesley Longman, Inc., 2000, p. 164.

Exercise 4: Wendy G. Lehnert, *Light on the Internet*. New York: Addison Wesley Longman, Inc., 1999, pp. 53, 55.

Exercise 5: Wendy G. Lehnert, *Light on the Internet*. New York: Addison Wesley Longman, Inc., 1999, pp. 60-62.

Exercise 6: Neil A. Campbell, Lawrence G. Mitchell, and Jane B. Reece, *Biology: Concepts & Connections,* 3rd edition. New York: Addison Wesley Longman, Inc., 2000, p. 357.

Exercise 7: Neil A. Campbell, Lawrence G. Mitchell, and Jane B. Reece, *Biology: Concepts & Connections,* 3rd edition. New York: Addison Wesley Longman, Inc., 2000, p430.

Exercise 8: John A. Garraty and Mark C. Carnes, *The American Nation,* 10th edition. New York: Addison Wesley Longman, Inc., 2000, p. 862

Exercise 9: John A. Garraty and Mark C. Carnes, *The American Nation,* 10th edition. New York: Addison Wesley Longman, Inc., 2000, pp. 878-879.